W9-AKY-149

Geometry

Test Booklet

1-888-854-MATH (6284)

www.MathUSee.com

Math·U·See

1-888-854-MATH (6284)
www.MathUSee.com

Copyright © 2009 by Steven P. Demme

All rights reserved. No part of this book may be reproduced, stored
in a retrieval system, or transmitted in any form by any means—electronic,
mechanical, photocopying, recording or otherwise.

In other words, thou shalt not steal.

Printed in the United States of America.

TESTS

Tests are primarily for evaluating a student's progress. If a student does well on the test, then he is ready to move on to the next lesson. If he does not do well, spend more time on that lesson and master it before moving to the new material. (The solutions for the tests are in the instruction manual.) Math is sequential and builds from concept to concept and from lesson to lesson. Master the material in each lesson before moving to the next topic.

The simplest way to solve a multiple-choice problem is to pretend there are no answers given and simply solve it, and then find your answer among those offered. But it is also a good idea to estimate the answer before doing any calculations and eliminate several of the possibilities.

When the potential answers have been narrowed, then solve the problem and choose the correct answer.

You will find that this form of testing measures your reasoning abilities as well as your math knowledge. It also requires more than a cursory knowledge of the material being tested. Let me encourage you to look upon these tests, not merely as exams to conquer and pass, but also as an opportunity to learn and stretch your knowledge about this particular topic.

This booklet also contains three unit tests and a final exam, which are not written in multiple-choice format. They are designed to help you, as you move through the course, to remember what you have already learned.

STANDARDIZED TESTS

The tests in this book have been written in the format most likely to be encountered on standardized tests. If the student is not familiar with the thinking skills employed in attacking multiple-choice answers, please spend some time explaining the different format and the different way of thinking that is required. Before attempting the SAT or ACT tests, it is recommended that the student complete *Algebra I*, *Geometry*, and most of *Algebra 2*.

Steve Demme

Circle your answer.

1. A point has:
    A. width
    B. no dimensions
    C. length
    D. height
    E. two dimensions

2. An infinite number of connected points is a(n):
    A. ray
    B. line segment
    C. plane
    D. endpoint
    E. line

3. The intersection of two lines is a(n):
    A. point
    B. plane
    C. line segment
    D. ray
    E. endpoint

4. A line has:
    A. length
    B. width
    C. length and width
    D. endpoints
    E. starting point

5. The number of points in a line:
    A. is the empty set
    B. is infinite
    C. varies according to the length of the line
    D. depends on the size of the point
    E. varies according to the width of the line

Use this diagram for #6–10.

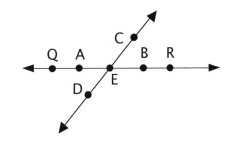

6. $\overrightarrow{AB}$ contains point:
    A. D
    B. C
    C. E
    D. M
    E. Q

7. $\overrightarrow{BA}$ contains point:
    A. Q
    B. R
    C. D
    D. C
    E. M

Use this diagram for #6–10.

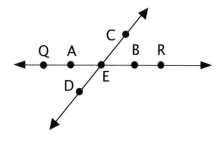

8. How many points are in $\overleftrightarrow{QR}$?
    A. 5
    B. 3
    C. none
    D. infinite
    E. 2

9. Which line segment is fully contained in $\overline{QB}$?
    A. $\overline{QR}$
    B. $\overline{DC}$
    C. $\overrightarrow{QB}$
    D. $\overrightarrow{BA}$
    E. $\overline{AB}$

10. $\overrightarrow{EC}$ travels in the opposite direction from:
    A. $\overrightarrow{DE}$
    B. $\overrightarrow{CE}$
    C. $\overrightarrow{DC}$
    D. $\overrightarrow{BE}$
    E. $\overrightarrow{EB}$

11. A geometric figure with no dimensions is a:
    A. ray
    B. line
    C. point
    D. line segment
    E. plane

12. Two amounts that are exactly the same are:
    A. similar
    B. congruent
    C. equal
    D. finite
    E. infinite

13. Two figures that have the same shape but different sizes are:
    A. similar
    B. congruent
    C. equal
    D. finite
    E. infinite

14. Two figures that are exactly the same shape and size are:
    A. similar
    B. congruent
    C. equal
    D. finite
    E. infinite

15. A figure with one definite endpoint is a(n):
    A. ray
    B. line
    C. point
    D. line segment
    E. plane

Circle your answer.

1. Two lines in the same
    plane are:
    A. an intersection
    B. lines
    C. collinear
    D. similar
    E. coplanar

2. The intersection of two planes is a(n):
    A. plane
    B. ray
    C. point
    D. line
    E. empty set

3. A plane has:
    A. length
    B. width
    C. length and width
    D. endpoints
    E. starting point

4. How many dimensions
    in a plane?
    A. 0
    B. 1
    C. 2
    D. 3
    E. 4

5. The overlap of two sets is a(n):
    A. intersection
    B. union
    C. empty set
    D. infinity
    E. plane

6. The combination of two sets
    is a(n):
    A. intersection
    B. union
    C. empty set
    D. infinity
    E. plane

7. The number of points in
    a plane is:
    A. the empty set
    B. infinite
    C. variable
    D. finite
    E. countable

8. Which symbol indicates no items
    in a set?
    A. $\cap$
    B. $\subset$
    C. $\varnothing$
    D. ∞
    E. $\cup$

9. Which symbol indicates intersection?
    - A. ∩
    - B. ⊂
    - C. ∅
    - D. ∞
    - E. ∪

10. Which symbol indicates union?
    - A. ∩
    - B. ⊂
    - C. ∅
    - D. ∞
    - E. ∪

Use this diagram for #11–15.

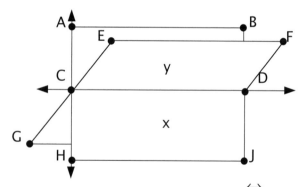

Given: Planes x and y intersect at $\overleftrightarrow{CD}$.

11. x ∩ y is:
    - A. $\overline{CD}$
    - B. $\overleftrightarrow{CD}$
    - C. $\overrightarrow{CD}$
    - D. $\overrightarrow{DC}$
    - E. $\overleftrightarrow{GE}$

12. $\overrightarrow{CA} \cup \overrightarrow{CH}$ is:
    - A. $\overline{AH}$
    - B. $\overline{CA}$
    - C. $\overleftrightarrow{AH}$
    - D. AC
    - E. $\overleftrightarrow{CD}$

13. Which of the following sets of points are in plane y?
    - A. E, F, B
    - B. B, C, G
    - C. G, C, H
    - D. E, C, H
    - E. F, D, E

14. Which line is not coplanar with $\overleftrightarrow{BJ}$?
    - A. $\overleftrightarrow{CD}$
    - B. $\overrightarrow{AB}$
    - C. $\overleftrightarrow{EG}$
    - D. $\overleftrightarrow{HJ}$
    - E. $\overrightarrow{AH}$

15. Which of the following points lies in plane y?
    - A. E
    - B. A
    - C. H
    - D. B
    - E. J

Use this diagram for #1–5.

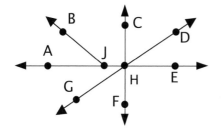

Circle your answer.

1. What is the vertex of ∠CHE?
   A. C
   B. H
   C. E
   D. J
   E. D

2. What is the vertex of ∠CHG?
   A. C
   B. H
   C. G
   D. J
   E. F

3. What is the vertex of ∠AJB?
   A. C
   B. A
   C. J
   D. B
   E. H

4. The common endpoint of $\overrightarrow{HA}$ and $\overrightarrow{HC}$ is:
   A. H
   B. A
   C. J
   D. C
   E. F

5. What angle lies between the rays described in #4?
   A. ∠ACH
   B. ∠HAC
   C. ∠BHC
   D. ∠GHC
   E. ∠AHC

6. The tool used to measure angles is a(n):
   A. compass
   B. protractor
   C. ruler
   D. calculator
   E. straight edge

7. Angles are measured in:
   A. inches
   B. millimeters
   C. degrees
   D. feet
   E. arcs

8. What angle would be formed by the rays $\overrightarrow{RS}$ and $\overrightarrow{RT}$? (not shown)
   - A. ∠RST
   - B. ∠SRT
   - C. ∠STR
   - D. ∠TSR
   - E. none of the above

9. "m∠2" is read as:
   - A. the middle of angle two
   - B. the measure of the angle is two
   - C. m is greater than two
   - D. the vertex of angle two
   - E. the measure of angle two

10. The measure of the angle is closest to:
    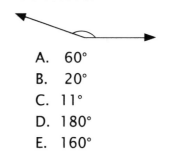
    - A. 90°
    - B. 45°
    - C. 11°
    - D. 80°
    - E. 130°

11. The measure of the angle is closest to:
    - A. 90°
    - B. 35°
    - C. 15°
    - D. 75°
    - E. 110°

12. The measure of the angle is closest to:
    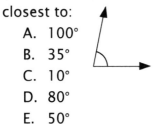
    - A. 100°
    - B. 35°
    - C. 10°
    - D. 80°
    - E. 50°

13. The measure of the angle is closest to:
    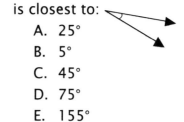
    - A. 85°
    - B. 50°
    - C. 170°
    - D. 95°
    - E. 130°

14. The measure of the angle is closest to:
    - A. 25°
    - B. 5°
    - C. 45°
    - D. 75°
    - E. 155°

15. The measure of the angle is closest to:
    - A. 60°
    - B. 20°
    - C. 11°
    - D. 180°
    - E. 160°

4

Use this diagram for #1–5.

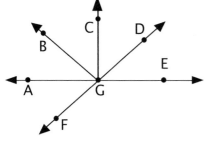

Given: m∠EGC = 90°;
$\overleftrightarrow{AE}$ is a straight line.

Circle your answer.

1. Which of the following is an
   obtuse angle?
   A. ∠EGD
   B. ∠DGE
   C. ∠CGE
   D. ∠BGE
   E. ∠AGF

2. Which angle is a right angle?
   A. ∠EGD
   B. ∠DGE
   C. ∠CGE
   D. ∠BGE
   E. ∠AGF

3. Which of the following is not
   an acute angle?
   A. ∠AGC
   B. ∠AGF
   C. ∠BGC
   D. ∠CGD
   E. ∠DGE

4. If m∠FGE is greater than 180°,
   what kind of angle is it?
   A. acute
   B. obtuse
   C. reflex
   D. right
   E. straight

5. What kind of angle is ∠AGE?
   A. acute
   B. obtuse
   C. reflex
   D. right
   E. straight

6. What is the vertex of ∠RST?
   A. R
   B. S
   C. T
   D. an infinite number of points
   E. can't tell from
      information given

7. How many degrees are there
   in ∠QRS if it is a right angle?
   A. 45°
   B. 90°
   C. 180°
   D. 100°
   E. can't tell from
      information given

8. How many degrees are there in ∠TUV
   if it is an obtuse angle?
   A. 90°
   B. 95°
   C. 180°
   D. 360°
   E. can't tell from
      information given

9. Which angle has the smallest measure?
    A. acute
    B. obtuse
    C. reflex
    D. right
    E. straight

10. Two roads cross at right angles. If a hiker walking along one road makes a right hand turn onto the other, how many degrees does he turn?
    A. 30°
    B. 180°
    C. 360°
    D. 90°
    E. 45°

Use this diagram for #11–15.

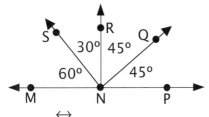

Given: $\overleftrightarrow{MP}$ is a straight line.

11. Which of the following is a right angle.
    A. ∠SNP
    B. ∠QNP
    C. ∠RNP
    D. ∠MNP
    E. ∠SNM

12. What is the sum of m∠SNR and m∠RNQ?
    A. 90°
    B. 120°
    C. 15°
    D. 60°
    E. 75°

13. If $\overrightarrow{NQ}$ was redrawn so that ∠QNP equaled 50°, what would the new measure of ∠RNQ be?
    A. 50°
    B. 40°
    C. 30°
    D. 95°
    E. can't tell from information given

14. Which of the following is the smallest obtuse angle listed?
    A. ∠MNQ
    B. ∠PNS
    C. ∠MNR
    D. ∠MNP
    E. ∠QNP

15. What is the smallest whole number of degrees that could be added to m∠MNR to make it a reflex angle?
    A. 1°
    B. 45°
    C. 91°
    D. 180°
    E. 360°

5

Circle your answer.

Use the diagram for #5–9.

1. Two lines in the same plane that never intersect are:
    A. parallel
    B. perpendicular
    C. bisectors
    D. collinear
    E. segments

Given: ABCD is a square.
(All corners are 90° angles.)

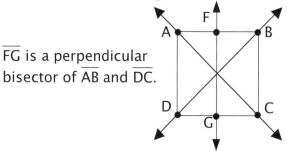

$\overline{FG}$ is a perpendicular bisector of $\overline{AB}$ and $\overline{DC}$.

2. Two lines that intersect and form a right angle are:
    A. parallel
    B. perpendicular
    C. bisectors
    D. collinear
    E. segments

5. Which of the following is true?
    A. AF = FB
    B. AF = AD
    C. FB = BC
    D. m ∠AFG = 85°
    E. none of the above

3. A line that forms a 90° angle with the original line is:
    A. parallel
    B. a segment
    C. collinear
    D. a ray
    E. perpendicular

6. Which pair of line segments is not perpendicular?
    A. $\overline{AD}$ and $\overline{AB}$
    B. $\overline{BC}$ and $\overline{AB}$
    C. $\overline{AB}$ and $\overline{FG}$
    D. $\overline{DA}$ and $\overline{GF}$
    E. $\overline{GF}$ and $\overline{GC}$

4. A line that cuts an angle in half is a(n):
    A. ray
    B. bisector
    C. segment
    D. vertex
    E. arc

7. Since $\overleftrightarrow{FG}$ is a perpendicular bisector of $\overline{DC}$, which statements are true?
    I.   DG = GC
    II. ∠DGF is a right angle
    III. DG = FG
    IV. G is the midpoint of $\overline{DC}$

    A. III only
    B. I, II
    C. I, II, IV
    D. II, III, IV
    E. IV only

8. Since ABCD is a square and given that $\overleftrightarrow{AC}$ bisects ∠FAD, what is the measure of ∠FAC?
   A. 90°
   B. 45°
   C. 30°
   D. 40°
   E. unknown

9. What is the measure of ∠BCA if ∠BCD is bisected by $\overleftrightarrow{AC}$?
   A. 90°
   B. 45°
   C. 30°
   D. 40°
   E. unknown

10. The symbol for perpendicular is:
    A. ‖   D. ∪
    B. ∩   E. ∅
    C. ⊥

11. The symbol for parallel is:
    A. ‖   D. ∪
    B. ∩   E. ∅
    C. ⊥

12. If two lines intersect and form a right angle, they are perpendicular. Which is also true?
    A. If two lines are perpendicular, they intersect and form a right angle.
    B. If two lines are parallel and form a right angle, they are perpendicular.
    C. If two lines are perpendicular, they are parallel.
    D. A right angle contains 180°.
    E. Two intersecting lines always form a right angle.

13. What tools are needed to bisect a line segment or an angle?
    I.   straight edge
    II. ruler
    III. compass
    IV. protractor

    A. II and III
    B. III and IV
    C. I and III
    D. II
    E. IV

14. When bisecting an angle, first place the compass point:
    A. on a point outside the ∠
    B. on a point inside the ∠
    C. at a point about one inch from the vertex
    D. at the vertex
    E. on a line ⊥ to one of the rays

15. If $\overline{QR}$ is a perpendicular bisector of $\overline{ST}$ at M, which of the following is **not** true?
    A. $\overline{SM} \cong \overline{MT}$
    B. ∠QMT is a right angle
    C. $\overline{QR} \parallel \overline{ST}$
    D. M is the midpoint of $\overline{ST}$
    E. four right angles are present

6

Circle your answer.

1. Two angles whose measures add up to 180° are called:
    A. straight
    B. complementary
    C. acute
    D. obtuse
    E. supplementary

2. Vertical angles are:
    A. supplementary
    B. complementary
    C. congruent
    D. adjacent
    E. obtuse

3. m∠XYZ = 35°. What is the measure of its complement?
    A. 145°
    B. 55°
    C. 35°
    D. 65°
    E. 125°

4. m∠GEF = 40°. What is the measure of its supplement?
    A. 60°
    B. 50°
    C. 140°
    D. 320°
    E. 40°

5. Angle A is 20° and angle B is 70°. What is their relationship?
    A. supplementary
    B. vertical
    C. reflexive
    D. coplanar
    E. complementary

Use this diagram for #6–10.

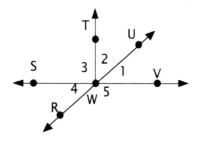

Given: $\overrightarrow{WT} \perp \overleftrightarrow{SV}$; $\overleftrightarrow{RU} \cap \overleftrightarrow{SV}$ at W.

6. ∠1 is adjacent to:
    A. ∠1
    B. ∠2 and ∠5
    C. ∠3
    D. ∠4
    E. ∠2

7. The sum of m∠1 and m∠2 is:
    A. 90°
    B. 180°
    C. 45°
    D. 360°
    E. can't tell from information given

Use this diagram for #6–10.

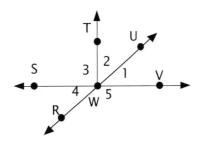

Use this diagram for #11–15.

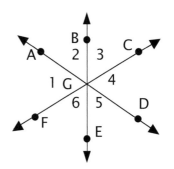

Given: $\overrightarrow{WT} \perp \overleftrightarrow{SV}$; $\overleftrightarrow{RU} \cap \overleftrightarrow{SV}$ at W.

Given: $\overleftrightarrow{FC}$, $\overleftrightarrow{AD}$, $\overleftrightarrow{BE}$ intersect at G.

8. The measure of ∠UWV is:
    A. 45°
    B. 30°
    C. 90°
    D. 35°
    E. can't tell from information given

    A. if the quantity in column I is greater.
    B. if the quantity in column II is greater.
    C. if the two quantities are equal.
    D. if the relationship cannot be determined from the information given.

9. ∠4 and what other angle are vertical angles?
    A. ∠3
    B. ∠4
    C. ∠2
    D. ∠1
    E. ∠TWV

Write the correct letter in the blank.

10. ∠SWT + ∠TWU + ∠UWV =
    A. 180°
    B. 360°
    C. 90°
    D. 100°
    E. can't tell from information given

	I	II	
11.	m∠2	m∠5	_____
12.	m∠4 + m∠5	136°	_____
13.	180°	m∠2 + m∠3	_____
14.	m∠2	m∠3	_____
15.	185°	sum of the measures of 2 right angles	_____

Use this diagram for #1–10.

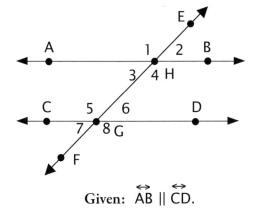

Given: $\overleftrightarrow{AB} \parallel \overleftrightarrow{CD}$.

Circle your answer.

1. ∠3 corresponds to:
   A. ∠2
   B. ∠4
   C. ∠5
   D. ∠7
   E. ∠8

2. If ∠2 = 80°, then ∠4 =
   A. 10°
   B. 20°
   C. 100°
   D. 280°
   E. 110°

3. m∠6 = m∠3 because:
   A. vertical angles
      are equal
   B. alternate interior angles
      are complementary
   C. they look parallel
   D. alternate exterior angles are
      congruent
   E. alternate interior angles are
      congruent

4. Which exterior angle corresponds
   to 6?
   A. ∠1
   B. ∠2
   C. ∠8
   D. ∠5
   E. ∠4

5. What is the relationship between
   ∠8 and ∠1?
   A. vertical
   B. corresponding
   C. alternate interior
   D. alternate exterior
   E. complementary

6. If we know the measure of ∠3,
   what other angles can we determine
   the measure of?
   A. none
   B. ∠1, 2, and 4
   C. ∠2
   D. ∠1
   E. ∠1, 2, 4, 5, 6, 7, and 8

7. If ∠6 = 65°, then ∠7 =
   A. 25°
   B. 30°
   C. 65°
   D. 115°
   E. can't tell from
      information given

8. ∠1 and ∠4 are:
   A. alternate interior
   B. alternate exterior
   C. corresponding
   D. vertical
   E. supplementary

9. ∠1 and ∠3 are:
    A. alternate interior
    B. alternate exterior
    C. corresponding
    D. vertical
    E. supplementary

10. $\overleftrightarrow{CD}$ is moved so that it is no longer parallel to $\overleftrightarrow{AB}$. m∠1 = 110°. What is the measure of ∠8?
    A. 110°
    B. 70°
    C. 20°
    D. 100°
    E. can't tell from information given

11. If two angles are supplementary, the sum of their measures is 180°. State the converse.
    A. If two angles are complementary, the sum of their measures is 90°.
    B. If two angles are supplementary, the sum of their measures is 90°.
    C. If the sum of two angles is 180°, they are supplementary.
    D. If the sum of two angles is 90°, they are supplementary.
    E. If you know the measure of one supplementary angle, you can find the measure of the other.

12. What is necessary to a diagram in order to have congruent alternate interior angles?
    A. parallel lines
    B. right angles
    C. obtuse angles
    D. acute angles
    E. perpendicular lines

13. Angle B = 45°. What is the measure of its alternate interior angle formed by parallel lines?
    A. 90°
    B. 135°
    C. 50°
    D. 45°
    E. 100°

14. Two parallel roads are crossed by a third that is perpendicular to both. How many right angles are formed?
    A. 1
    B. 2
    C. 4
    D. 8
    E. none

15. Alternate interior angles formed by parallel lines are:
    A. vertical
    B. congruent
    C. supplementary
    D. complementary
    E. obtuse

8

Circle your answer.

1. Which of the following are parallelograms?
   I. square
   II. rhombus
   III. trapezoid
   IV. prism
   V. rectangle

   A. I, II, III
   B. I, II, III, V
   C. II, III
   D. II, IV
   E. I, II, V

2. Which of the following is true?
   A. A trapezoid is a parallelogram.
   B. A rhombus is a square.
   C. All squares are rectangles.
   D. All rectangles are squares.
   E. A rhombus has sides of unequal length.

3. Which of the following is **not** true?
   A. All rhombuses are parallelograms.
   B. A square is a quadrilateral.
   C. A triangle is trilateral.
   D. A trapezoid must have a right angle.
   E. A rectangle is one kind of parallelogram.

4. In order to find the perimeter of a quadrilateral, which measurement(s) are needed?
   A. angles
   B. width
   C. area
   D. height
   E. length of each side

5. Any four-sided figure can be called a:
   A. quadrilateral
   B. square
   C. rectangle
   D. rhombus
   E. parallelogram

6. The sum of the interior angles of a triangle is:
   A. 360°
   B. 90°
   C. 270°
   D. 180°
   E. variable by triangle

7. Identify a shape with four right angles and four congruent sides.
   A. prism
   B. rhombus
   C. triangle
   D. square
   E. trapezoid

8. Identify a shape with four congruent sides and no right angles:
   A. rectangle
   B. rhombus
   C. triangle
   D. square
   E. trapezoid

9. The sum of the interior angles of a quadrilateral is:
   A. 360°   D. 180°
   B. 90°   E. variable
   C. 270°

10. Identify a shape with only one pair of parallel sides and no right angles.
    A. quadrilateral
    B. trapezoid
    C. rectangle
    D. rhombus
    E. parallelogram

Use the following figures for #11–15.

Figure A

Figure B

Figure C

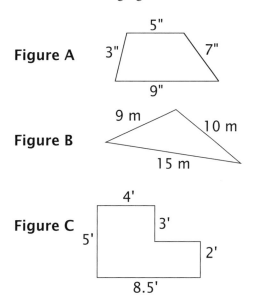

Figure D 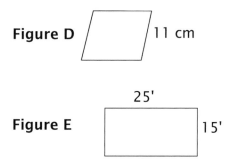 11 cm

Figure E 25' 15'

11. The perimeter of figure A is:
    A. 24"   D. 78"
    B. 27"   E. 19"
    C. 35"

12. The perimeter of figure B is:
    A. 45 m   D. 60 m
    B. 14.5 m E. 29 m
    C. 34 m

13. All angles in figure C are right angles. The perimeter is:
    A. 22.5'   D. 27'
    B. 26.5'   E. 20'
    C. 42.5'

14. Figure D is a rhombus. The perimeter is:
    A. 22 cm   D. 11 cm
    B. 44 cm   E. 33 cm
    C. 121 cm

15. Figure E is a rectangle. The perimeter is:
    A. 375'   D. 55'
    B. 40'   E. 80'
    C. 65'

Circle your answer.

1. The area of a parallelogram is found by multiplying the base times the:
    A. average base
    B. height
    C. one-half the height
    D. base
    E. perimeter

2. The height of a quadrilateral is always:
    A. parallel to the base
    B. congruent to the base
    C. unknown
    D. one-half the base
    E. perpendicular to the base

3. To find the area of a triangle, find the area of a rectangle with the same base and height and:
    A. multiply by two
    B. divide by two
    C. take the average of base and height
    D. use that area for the triangle
    E. add one-half

4. When finding the area of a trapezoid, it is necessary to:
    A. multiply by one-half
    B. divide by two
    C. know the length of all four sides
    D. find the average base
    E. none of the above

5. The angle formed by the height and the base of a triangle is:
    A. 90°
    B. 180°
    C. 45°
    D. 60°
    E. variable

6. One side of a square is 10 feet. What is its area?
    A. 40 ft
    B. 40 ft^2
    C. 100 ft^2
    D. 100 ft
    E. not enough information

7. A trapezoid has one base of 7" and a height of 10". What is its area?
    A. 70 ft^2
    B. 34 ft
    C. 45 ft^2
    D. 45 ft
    E. not enough information

8. A triangle has a base of 8 m and a height of 4 m. What is its area?
    A. 32 m^2
    B. 32 m
    C. 12 m^2
    D. 16 m^2
    E. not enough information

9. The base of a rectangle is 15 and the height is 3. What is its area?
    A. 36 units²
    B. 18 units
    C. 45 units²
    D. 22.5 units²
    E. not enough information

10. One side of a rhombus is 9 ft. What is its area?
    A. 81 ft²
    B. 36 ft²
    C. 40.5 ft²
    D. 18 ft²
    E. not enough information

Use the following figures for #11–15.

Figure A
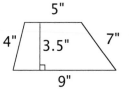

Figure B
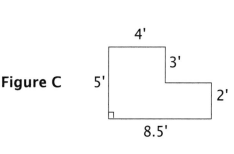

Figure C

Figure D

Figure E

11. The area of figure A is:
    A. 24.5 in²
    B. 24 in²
    C. 31.5 in²
    D. 17.5 in²
    E. 12.25 in²

12. The area of figure B is:
    A. 45 m²
    B. 34 m²
    C. 90 m²
    D. 17 m²
    E. 34 m

13. All angles in figure C are right angles. The area is:
    A. 25 ft²
    B. 34 ft²
    C. 29 ft²
    D. 24 ft²
    E. 27 ft²

14. Figure D is a rhombus. The area is:
    A. 22 cm²
    B. 44 cm²
    C. 121 cm
    D. 11 cm
    E. 110 cm²

15. Figure E is a rectangle. The area is:
    A. 375 ft²
    B. 40 ft²
    C. 65 ft
    D. 55 ft
    E. 80 ft²

Circle your answer.

1. A triangle has angles of 28°, 16°, and 136°. The triangle is:
    A. right
    B. equilateral
    C. acute
    D. obtuse
    E. impossible to draw

2. A triangle has sides with lengths of 6, 6, and 7 units. The triangle is:
    A. equilateral
    B. scalene
    C. isosceles
    D. right
    E. impossible to draw

3. A triangle has angles of 50°, 60°, and 70°. The triangle is:
    A. equilateral
    B. acute
    C. isosceles
    D. right
    E. impossible to draw

4. A right triangle has an angle measuring 28°. It also has an angle of:
    A. 30°
    B. 152°
    C. 62°
    D. 118°
    E. 60°

5. A triangle with sides measuring 5, 8, and 10 units is described as:
    A. right
    B. scalene
    C. isosceles
    D. equilateral
    E. impossible to draw

6. A triangle with angles of 61°, 62°, and 61° is:
    A. right
    B. equilateral
    C. acute
    D. isosceles
    E. impossible to draw

7. It is possible for a triangle to be:
    A. acute and right
    B. acute and equilateral
    C. obtuse and right
    D. isosceles and scalene
    E. equiangular and obtuse

8. The length of one side of a triangle is 12 and another is 7. Which of the following is the shortest possible whole number length of the third leg?
    A. 7
    B. 5
    C. 6
    D. 8
    E. 19

9. A triangle with sides measuring
    2, 2, and 5 units is:
    A. equilateral
    B. scalene
    C. right
    D. isosceles
    E. impossible to draw

10. It is possible for a triangle to be:
    A. isosceles and right
    B. acute and right
    C. obtuse and right
    D. have two obtuse angles
    E. equiangular and obtuse

11. A triangle with two 60° angles is:
    A. right
    B. isosceles
    C. equilateral
    D. scalene
    E. obtuse

12. A triangle with angles of 74°
    and 16° is:
    A. equilateral
    B. obtuse
    C. isosceles
    D. right
    E. impossible to draw

13. It is possible for a triangle to be:
    A. isosceles and acute
    B. equilateral and right
    C. obtuse and right
    D. acute and right
    E. isosceles and scalene

14. Which triangle has three
    equal sides?
    A. right
    B. equilateral
    C. scalene
    D. isosceles
    E. obtuse

15. An isosceles triangle has an
    angle of 34°. Its other two angles
    could be:
    A. 73° and 73°
    B. 28° and 28°
    C. 34° and 90°
    D. 28° and 90°
    E. 68° and 68°

UNIT TEST **Lessons 1–10** (100 points possible)

I. Fill in the blank with the best answer. (2 points each)

1. _____ Where two or more lines share a common point.

2. _____ Having the same size and shape.

3. _____ A set with no members.

4. _____ A polygon with three sides.

5. _____ Any two angles which add up to 180°.

6. _____ An angle with a measure greater than 180° and less than 360°.

7. _____ A line that cuts an angle or segment in half.

8. _____ The union of two rays with a common endpoint.

II.   In the space below, do the following: (14 points)

    1. Draw an angle with a measure of 230°.

    2. Draw an 80° angle, and then using your compass, construct its bisector.

III.   Give a quick definition and sketch for each of the following: (8 points)

    1. isosceles triangle

    2. scalene triangle

IV.   Give the perimeter and area for the trapezoid. (6 points)

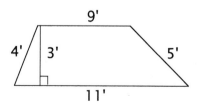

V.   Use the drawing to answer questions #1–12. (3 points each)

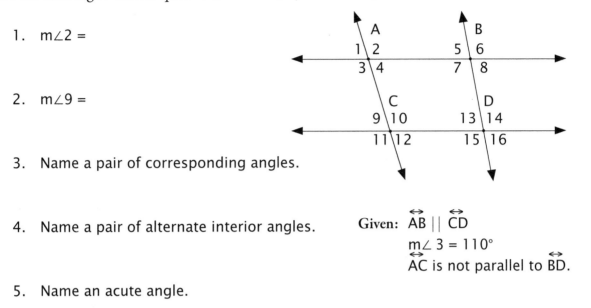

1.   m∠2 =

2.   m∠9 =

3.   Name a pair of corresponding angles.

4.   Name a pair of alternate interior angles.

Given: $\overleftrightarrow{AB} \parallel \overleftrightarrow{CD}$
    m∠ 3 = 110°
    $\overleftrightarrow{AC}$ is not parallel to $\overleftrightarrow{BD}$.

5.   Name an acute angle.

6.   Is ∠13 ≅ ∠9?   Why or why not?

7.   Name two points on this drawing that are not collinear.

8.   What is the vertex of ∠3?

9.   How many points are in line AB?

10.   How many dimensions does line AB have?

11.   Name an angle that is supplementary to ∠1.

12.   Name the vertical angle that is paired with ∠12.

VI. If AB = 6 inches and BC = 2 inches, what is the area of triangle ABC? (5 points)

VII. Name all the shapes that have two pairs of parallel sides. (8 points)

VIII. Given: set A = { 2, 3, 4, 5} and set B = { 3, 4, 5, 6}. Answer the questions. (7 points)

1. What is A ∪ B?

2. Is set A a subset of set B?   Why or why not?

Circle your answer.

1. In a regular seven–sided polygon, how many diagonals can be drawn from one vertex?
    A. 5
    B. 3
    C. 4
    D. 6
    E. 7

2. In a regular dodecagon (12 sides), how many triangles can be formed by drawing diagonals from one vertex?
    A. 10
    B. 12
    C. 11
    D. 16
    E. 8

3. What is the sum of the interior angles of an 11–sided regular polygon?
    A. 1800°
    B. 1980°
    C. 360°
    D. 1620°
    E. 180°

4. What is the name of a regular polygon with five sides?
    A. pentagon
    B. octagon
    C. decagon
    D. hexagon
    E. dodecagon

5. What is the sum of the exterior angles of a regular polygon? (N = number of sides)
    A. 360°
    B. 180°
    C. (N – 2)°
    D. (180 x N)°
    E. (N – 2) x 180°

6. What is the measure of one interior angle of an octagon?
    A. 45°
    B. 135°
    C. 180°
    D. 55°
    E. 100°

7. The draftsman drew a regular polygon with 100 sides. The exterior angles add up to:
    A. 16,200°
    B. 100°
    C. 1800°
    D. 180°
    E. 360°

8. In the regular polygon shown, m∠a equals 36°. What is m∠b?
    A. 30°
    B. 54°
    C. 36°
    D. 72°
    E. 108°

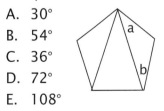

9. In the regular octagon shown, AB bisects vertex A. What is m∠a?

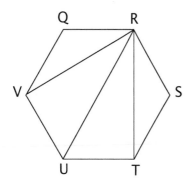

   A. 135°
   B. 51.5°
   C. 45°
   D. 90°
   E. 67.5°

Use this diagram for #10 –15.

Given: QRSTUV is a regular polygon.

10. What is the sum of the interior angles of the hexagon?
   A. 360°
   B. 720°
   C. 1080°
   D. 540°
   E. 490°

11. What is the measure of one exterior angle of the hexagon?
   A. 60°
   B. 30°
   C. 90°
   D. 45°
   E. 120°

12. If a line is drawn bisecting vertex S, what is the measure of each of the new angles formed?
   A. 120°
   B. 40°
   C. 60°
   D. 45°
   E. 50.5°

13. If the measure of ∠QRV is 30°, what is the measure of ∠QVR?
   A. 35°
   B. 25°
   C. 60°
   D. 30°
   E. 210°

14. What is the measure of ∠RVU?
   A. 30°
   B. 90°
   C. 160°
   D. 45°
   E. 95°

15. If the four angles at vertex R are congruent, what is the measure of ∠TRU?
   A. 30°
   B. 60°
   C. 35°
   D. 40°
   E. 25°

12

Circle your answer.

1. What is the perimeter of a circle called?
    A. circumference
    B. diameter
    C. chord
    D. area
    E. tangent

2. The central angle of a circle is 50°. What is the measure of the major arc formed by the angle?
    A. 50°
    B. 310°
    C. 360°
    D. 25°
    E. 155°

3. A circle's longest chord is its:
    A. radius
    B. diameter
    C. tangent
    D. perimeter
    E. circumference

4. A line that touches a circle at only one point is a(n):
    A. chord
    B. tangent
    C. arc
    D. circle
    E. ellipse

5. What is the relationship of a tangent and a radius that both intersect a circle at a point H on the circumference of the circle?
    A. They are parallel.
    B. They form a straight line.
    C. They are perpendicular.
    D. The radius is one-half the tangent.
    E. no predictable relationship

6. A pentagon is drawn inside a circle and touches it at five places. The pentagon is _____ the circle. What words go in the blank?
    A. intercepted by
    B. tangent to
    C. supplementary to
    D. circumscribed in
    E. inscribed in

7. A pie-shaped section of a circle is known in geometry as a(n):
    A. chord
    B. arc
    C. wedge
    D. sector
    E. triangle

8. A line that intersects a circle in exactly two points is a(n):
    A. secant
    B. chord
    C. tangent
    D. radius
    E. sector

9. A piece of the circumference of a circle is a(n):
   A. sector
   B. secant
   C. arc
   D. chord
   E. ellipse

10. A minor arc has a measure of 48°. What is the measure of the inscribed angle that intercepts the arc?
   A. 312°
   B. 156°
   C. 168°
   D. 24°
   E. 48°

Use this diagram for #11 –15.

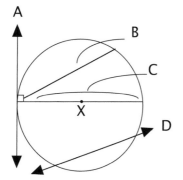

Given: X is the center of the circle.

11. Which letter indicates a diameter?
   A. A
   B. B
   C. C
   D. D
   E. none of the above

12. Which letter indicates a chord?
   A. A
   B. B
   C. C
   D. D
   E. none of the above

13. Which letter indicates a secant?
   A. A
   B. B
   C. C
   D. D
   E. none of the above

14. Which letter indicates a tangent?
   A. A
   B. B
   C. C
   D. D
   E. none of the above

15. Which letter indicates a radius?
   A. A
   B. B
   C. C
   D. D
   E. none of the above

Circle your answer.

1. Half the diameter of a circle is the:
    A. circumference
    B. radius
    C. chord
    D. secant
    E. tangent

2. The perimeter of a circle is the same as the:
    A. circumference
    B. radius
    C. chord
    D. secant
    E. area

3. The formula for the area of a circle is:
    A. πr^2
    B. $2\pi r$
    C. πd
    D. $\frac{1}{2} bh$
    E. $\frac{1}{2} X \cdot \frac{1}{2} Y \cdot \pi$

4. The formula for the circumference of a circle is:
    A. πr^2
    B. $2\pi r$
    C. $\frac{1}{2} \pi d$
    D. $\frac{1}{2} bh$
    E. $\frac{1}{2} X \cdot \frac{1}{2} Y \cdot \pi$

5. The formula for the area of an ellipse is:
    A. πr^2
    B. $2\pi r$
    C. $\frac{1}{2} \pi d$
    D. $\frac{1}{2} bh$
    E. $\frac{1}{2}$ long axis $\cdot \frac{1}{2}$ short axis $\cdot \pi$

6. How many minutes are there in a degree?
    A. 30'
    B. 60'
    C. 120'
    D. 360'
    E. 90'

7. The equator is a line of:
    A. area
    B. diameter
    C. distance
    D. longitude
    E. latitude

8. The north-south line going through Greenwich, England, is:
    A. the equator
    B. a line of latitude
    C. the prime meridian
    D. the diameter
    E. the international date line

9. What is the area of a circle with a radius of 3 units?
   - A. 9.42 units^2
   - B. 18.84 units^2
   - C. 28.26 units^2
   - D. 9 units^2
   - E. 36 units^2

10. What is the circumference of a circle with a diameter of 6 units?
   - A. 9.42 units
   - B. 18.84 units
   - C. 28.26 units
   - D. 123.04 units
   - E. 36 units

11. What is the fractional value of π?
   - A. 22/7
   - B. 1/3
   - C. 3/14
   - D. 7/22
   - E. none of the above

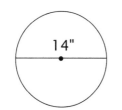

12. What is the area of the circle shown above? Use the fractional form of π.
   - A. 22 in^2
   - B. 44 in^2
   - C. 154 in^2
   - D. 616 in^2
   - E. none of the above

13. What is the circumference of the circle shown for #12? Use the fractional form of π.
   - A. 22 in
   - B. 44 in
   - C. 154 in
   - D. 616 in
   - E. none of the above

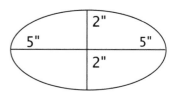

14. What is the area of the ellipse shown above? Use the decimal form of π.
   - A. 21.98 in^2
   - B. 31.4 in^2
   - C. 314 in^2
   - D. 153.86 in^2
   - E. none of the above

15. What is the area of a circle with a diameter of 8 units? Use the decimal form of π.
   - A. 12.56 units^2
   - B. 25.12 units^2
   - C. 50.24 units^2
   - D. 200.96 units^2
   - E. none of the above

Circle your answer.

1. The basic formula for volume is to multiply the height times:
   A. the base
   B. the area of the base
   C. the circumference of the base
   D. the height
   E. the radius of the base

2. All the faces of a cube are:
   A. rectangles
   B. regular polygons
   C. congruent
   D. squares
   E. all of the above

3. The lines where the faces of a rectangular solid meet are called:
   A. solids
   B. vertices
   C. bases
   D. arcs
   E. edges

4. What is the number of vertices in a cube?
   A. 6
   B. 12
   C. 8
   D. 4
   E. 16

5. With what kind of units is volume measured?
   A. feet
   B. inches
   C. square
   D. cubic
   E. solid

6. The formula for the volume of a cylinder is:
   A. $\pi r^2 \times h$
   B. πr^2
   C. $2\pi r^2$
   D. bh
   E. $2(\pi r^2) \times h$

7. The volume of a cube with edges 6" long is:
   A. 36 in^3
   B. 216 in^3
   C. 216 in^2
   D. 72 in^3
   E. 72 in^2

8. The flat surfaces that make up a rectangular solid are:
   A. solids
   B. vertices
   C. bases
   D. faces
   E. edges

9. The dimensions of a rectangular solid are 3 x 4 x 9. What is its volume?
    A. 216 units^3
    B. 16 units^2
    C. 108 units^3
    D. 108 units^2
    E. 63 units^3

10. A cylinder has a radius of 10 meters and a height of 6 meters. What is its volume?
    A. 188.4 m^3
    B. 188.4 m^2
    C. 60 m^3
    D. 1,884 m^2
    E. 1,884 m^3

11. What is the number of faces in a rectangular solid?
    A. 6
    B. 12
    C. 8
    D. 4
    E. 16

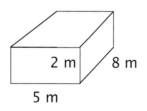

12. What is the volume of the rectangular solid shown above?
    A. 160 m^3
    B. 80 m^2
    C. 15 m^2
    D. 42 m^3
    E. 80 m^3

10 in

13. What is the volume of the cube shown above?
    A. 100 in^3
    B. 1000 in^3
    C. 200 in^2
    D. 30 in^3
    E. 100 in^2

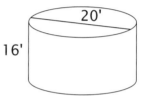

14. What is the volume of the cylinder shown above?
    A. 10,004.8 ft^3
    B. 5,024 ft^3
    C. 5,024 ft^2
    D. 502.4 ft^3
    E. 320 ft^3

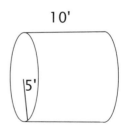

15. What is the volume of the cylinder shown above?
    A. 314 ft^3
    B. 1,570 ft^3
    C. 785 ft^3
    D. 157 ft^3
    E. 50 ft^2

Circle your answer.

1. The sides, or faces of a pyramid are:
   A. triangles
   B. squares
   C. trapezoids
   D. rectangles
   E. rhombuses

2. The height of a pyramid perpendicular to the base is the:
   A. slant height
   B. altitude
   C. diameter
   D. vertex
   E. none of the above

3. The height of a face of a pyramid is the:
   A. slant height
   B. altitude
   C. diameter
   D. vertex
   E. none of the above

4. A figure with lateral surfaces that are parallelograms and two parallel bases is called a:
   A. cone
   B. pyramid
   C. sphere
   D. prism
   E. none of the above

Write the correct letter in the blank. Assume that all units of measure are the same.
   A. if value in column I is greater.
   B. if value in column II is greater.
   C. if the two values are equal.
   D. if not enough information is given to determine the relationship.

	I	II	
5.	volume of a cylinder with diameter of 3 and height of 4	volume of a cone with diameter of 3 and height of 4	_____
6.	volume of a pyramid with base area of 16	volume of a cone with base area of 16	_____
7.	volume of a sphere with radius of 4	volume of a cone with base diameter of 8 and a height of 4	_____
8.	volume of a sphere with radius of 50	volume of a sphere with diameter of 100	_____
9.	volume of a cylinder with base area of 4 and height of 10	volume of a rectangular solid with base area of 10 and height of 8	_____

10. Which formula is used to find the volume of a sphere?
    A. V = Bh
    B. V = 1/3 Bh
    C. V = πr²
    D. V = 4/3 πr²
    E. none of the above

11. Which formula is used to find the volume of a cone?
    A. V = Bh
    B. V = 1/3 Bh
    C. V = πr²
    D. V = 4/3 πr²
    E. none of the above

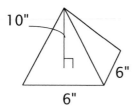

12. What is the volume of the pyramid shown?
    A. 120 in³
    B. 360 in³
    C. 22 in³
    D. 3,600 in³
    E. 46 in³

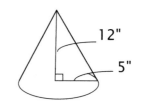

13. What is the volume of the cone shown?
    A. 120 in³
    B. 40 in³
    C. 20 in³
    D. 942 in³
    E. 314 in³

14. What is the volume of the prism shown?
    A. 36 ft³
    B. 72 ft³
    C. 5,216 ft³
    D. 13 ft³
    E. 144 ft³

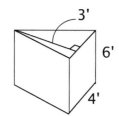

radius = 6 meters

15. What is the volume of the sphere shown?
    A. 150.72 m³
    B. 904.32 m³
    C. 226.08 m³
    D. 288 m³
    E. 2,712.96 m³

Circle your answer.

1. How many faces does a cube or rectangular solid have?
    A. 3
    B. 4
    C. 5
    D. 6
    E. varies

2. How many faces does a pyramid with a square base have?
    A. 3
    B. 4
    C. 5
    D. 6
    E. varies

3. How many faces does a pyramid with a triangular base have?
    A. 3
    B. 4
    C. 5
    D. 6
    E. varies

4. To find the surface area of a cylinder, add the areas of:
    A. one circle and a rectangle
    B. three circles
    C. two circles and a rectangle
    D. two circles and a trapezoid
    E. three parallelograms

5. Surface area is measured in:
    A. single units
    B. degrees
    C. cubic units
    D. square units
    E. minutes

6. What is the surface area of a cube with an edge of 7 inches?
    A. 294 in^2
    B. 294 in^3
    C. 42 in^3
    D. 42 in^2
    E. 196 in^2

7. A room is 12 ft x 14 ft with an 8 ft high ceiling. What is the surface area of the walls, floor, and ceiling?
    A. 752 ft^2
    B. 1,344 ft^3
    C. 520 ft^2
    D. 376 ft^2
    E. 376 ft^3

8. What is the surface area of a cylinder with a radius of 5 meters and a height of 10 meters?
    A. 471 m^2
    B. 2,355 m^2
    C. 345.4 m^2
    D. 50 m
    E. 785 m^3

9. What is the surface area of a pyramid with a 6" square base and a a slant height of 9"?
   A. 324 in³
   B. 324 in²
   C. 252 in²
   D. 144 in²
   E. 108 in²

10. A rectangular solid has edges measuring 3, 4, and 6 units. What is its surface area?
   A. 54 units³
   B. 108 units²
   C. 108 units³
   D. 30 units²
   E. 42 units²

11. The area of the square base of a pyramid is 100 ft². The slant height is 20 ft. What is the surface area of the solid?
   A. 400 ft²
   B. 500 ft²
   C. 2,000 ft²
   D. 1,000 ft²
   E. none of the above

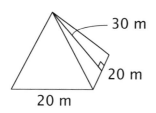

12. What is the surface area of the pyramid?
   A. 1,600 m²
   B. 2,800 m²
   C. 70 m³
   D. 12,000 m²
   E. 1,000 m²

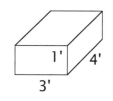

13. What is the surface area of the rectangular solid?
   A. 12 ft²
   B. 8 ft²
   C. 19 ft²
   D. 38 ft²
   E. 38 ft³

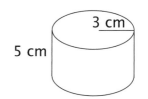

14. What is the surface area of the cylinder?
   A. 131.88 cm²
   B. 122.46 cm²
   C. 150.72 cm²
   D. 141.3 cm²
   E. 141.3 cm³

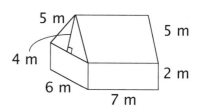

15. What is the surface area of the solid?
   A. 230 m²
   B. 168 m³
   C. 170 m²
   D. 115 m²
   E. 188 m²

17

Circle your answer.

1. If a whole number is a perfect square, its square root is:
   A. a radical
   B. always negative
   C. a whole number
   D. less than one
   E. always even

5. $(5\sqrt{X})(6\sqrt{Y}) =$
   A. $30\sqrt{X+Y}$
   B. $30\sqrt{XY}$
   C. $11\sqrt{XY}$
   D. $30\sqrt{X-Y}$
   E. cannot be simplified

2. The square root of six times the square root of six equals:
   A. 3
   B. 6
   C. 12
   D. 36
   E. –6

6. $6\sqrt{3} + 4\sqrt{3} =$
   A. 90
   B. 30
   C. $24\sqrt{3}$
   D. $10\sqrt{3}$
   E. cannot be simplified

3. $\sqrt{R} \cdot \sqrt{S} =$
   A. $\sqrt{R+S}$
   B. $\sqrt{RS}$
   C. RS
   D. $2\sqrt{RS}$
   E. cannot be simplified

7. $(3\sqrt{5})(3\sqrt{5}) =$
   A. 45
   B. 225
   C. $9\sqrt{5}$
   D. 30
   E. cannot be simplified

4. $\sqrt{R} + \sqrt{S} =$
   A. $\sqrt{R+S}$
   B. $\sqrt{RS}$
   C. R + S
   D. $2\sqrt{R+S}$
   E. cannot be simplified

8. $\sqrt{45} =$
   A. $5\sqrt{3}$
   B. $3\sqrt{5}$
   C. 15
   D. 45
   E. cannot be simplified

9. $\sqrt{24}$ =
   A. 5
   B. $2\sqrt{4}$
   C. $2\sqrt{6}$
   D. $6\sqrt{4}$
   E. cannot be simplified

13. $5\sqrt{7} + 4\sqrt{2}$ =
   A. $9\sqrt{14}$
   B. $9\sqrt{7}$
   C. 63
   D. $40\sqrt{14}$
   E. cannot be simplified

10. $\sqrt{42}$ =
   A. $7\sqrt{6}$
   B. $4\sqrt{14}$
   C. $2\sqrt{21}$
   D. 21
   E. cannot be simplified

14. $2\sqrt{3} + 3\sqrt{3} + 6\sqrt{3}$ =
   A. 33
   B. $11\sqrt{3}$
   C. $11\sqrt{18}$
   D. $36\sqrt{3}$
   E. cannot be simplified

11. $\dfrac{24\sqrt{18}}{6\sqrt{9}}$ =
   A. $4\sqrt{2}$
   B. 24
   C. 48
   D. $4\sqrt{3}$
   E. cannot be simplified

15. $(5\sqrt{3})(4\sqrt{2})$ =
   A. 120
   B. $9\sqrt{6}$
   C. 60
   D. $20\sqrt{6}$
   E. cannot be simplified

12. $\dfrac{15\sqrt{8}}{5\sqrt{2}}$ =
   A. $3\sqrt{2}$
   B. 12
   C. 6
   D. $3\sqrt{8}$
   E. cannot be simplified

Circle your answer.

1. If a and b are legs and c is the hypotenuse, the Pythagorean theorem can be written as:
   A. $\sqrt{a} + \sqrt{b} = \sqrt{c}$
   B. $a^2 + c^2 = b^2$
   C. $\sqrt{a} + \sqrt{b} = c^2$
   D. $a^2 + b^2 = c^2$
   E. $a + b = c$

2. If the square of the hypotenuse is equal to the sum of the squares of the legs, we know:
   A. the hypotenuse is twice as long as one of the legs
   B. the triangle is equilateral
   C. the triangle is a right triangle
   D. the triangle is congruent to other triangles with the same relationship
   E. none of the above

3. If the legs of a right triangle are 3 and 2, the hypotenuse is closest to:
   A. 2
   B. 8
   C. 5
   D. 4
   E. 6

4. If the legs of a right triangle are A and B, the length of the hypotenuse is:
   A. $A^2 + B^2$
   B. $A + B$
   C. $\sqrt{A^2 + B^2}$
   D. $\sqrt{A + B}$
   E. $\sqrt{AB}$

5. A right triangle has legs of 3 and 7. What is the length of the hypotenuse?
   A. $\sqrt{5}$
   B. $\sqrt{58}$
   C. $2\sqrt{29}$
   D. 58
   E. $\sqrt{21}$

6. A right triangle has legs of 4 and 6. What is the length of the hypotenuse in simplest form?
   A. 52
   B. 10
   C. $\sqrt{10}$
   D. $\sqrt{52}$
   E. $2\sqrt{13}$

7. A triangle has legs of 6, 8, and 10. Which of the following is true?
   A. It has an obtuse angle.
   B. It is not a right triangle.
   C. It is a right triangle.
   D. None of the angles can be determined.
   E. It is equilateral.

8. A triangle has legs of 5, 9, and 12. Which of the following do you know to be true?
   A. It has no obtuse angle.
   B. It is not a right triangle.
   C. It is a right triangle.
   D. It is an isosceles triangle.
   E. It is an equilateral triangle.

9. How many degrees are there in a right angle?
   A. 360°
   B. 180°
   C. 90°
   D. 45°
   E. 80°

10. The longest side of a right triangle is the
    A. hypotenuse
    B. leg
    C. theorem
    D. apothem
    E. height

11. In right triangle ABC, one leg $\overline{AB}$ has a length of 5 and the hypotenuse $\overline{BC}$ has a length of $\sqrt{61}$. What is the length of the leg $\overline{AC}$?
    A. $\sqrt{61}$
    B. $\sqrt{10}$
    C. $\sqrt{86}$
    D. 6
    E. $2\sqrt{43}$

12. In right triangle DEF, one leg $\overline{DE}$ has a length of 12 and the hypotenuse $\overline{EF}$ has a length of 13. What is the length of the leg $\overline{DF}$?
    A. 25
    B. 5
    C. 1
    D. $\sqrt{313}$
    E. $3\sqrt{35}$

Use this diagram for #13–15.

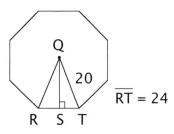

$\overline{RT} = 24$

Given: Figure is a regular polygon.
$\overline{QS}$ is the apothem.
$\overline{QS}$ bisects $\overline{RT}$.

13. What is the length of line segment $\overline{QS}$?
    A. 16
    B. 8
    C. $2\sqrt{5}$
    D. 20
    E. $2\sqrt{71}$

14. What is the area of triangle RQT?
    A. 96 units²
    B. 192 units²
    C. $2\sqrt{5}$ units²
    D. $24\sqrt{5}$ units²
    E. 240 units²

15. What is the total area of the polygon?
    A. 768 units²
    B. 192 units²
    C. 1,152 units²
    D. $192\sqrt{5}$ units²
    E. 1,536 units²

Circle your answer.

1. A radical cannot be used in a(n):
   A. numerator
   B. denominator
   C. fraction
   D. equation
   E. hypotenuse

2. The form of an expression may be changed by multiplying it by another expression equal to:
   A. −1
   B. 2
   C. 0
   D. $\sqrt{2}$
   E. 1

3. When adding two fractions, first find the:
   A. common denominator.
   B. numerator.
   C. hypotenuse.
   D. apothem.
   E. radical.

4. $\dfrac{5}{\sqrt{3}} =$

   A. $\dfrac{5\sqrt{3}}{3}$

   B. $\dfrac{5\sqrt{3}}{9}$

   C. $\dfrac{\sqrt{15}}{3}$

   D. $\dfrac{\sqrt{15}}{9}$

   E. $5\sqrt{3}$

5. $\dfrac{8\sqrt{2}}{\sqrt{4}} =$

   A. $2\sqrt{2}$

   B. $8\sqrt{8}$

   C. $\dfrac{\sqrt{8}}{16}$

   D. $4\sqrt{2}$

   E. $\dfrac{\sqrt{2}}{8}$

6. $\dfrac{4\sqrt{3}}{\sqrt{8}} =$

   A. $\dfrac{\sqrt{6}}{2}$

   B. $\sqrt{6}$

   C. $2\sqrt{6}$

   D. $2\sqrt{3}$

   E. $4\sqrt{3}$

7. $\dfrac{5\sqrt{5}}{\sqrt{5}} =$

   A. $\dfrac{5\sqrt{5}}{5}$

   B. 5

   C. 25

   D. $5\sqrt{5}$

   E. $25\sqrt{5}$

8. $\dfrac{3\sqrt{7}}{\sqrt{10}} =$

   A. $\dfrac{3\sqrt{70}}{10}$

   B. $\dfrac{3\sqrt{70}}{100}$

   C. $\dfrac{30\sqrt{7}}{10}$

   D. $3\sqrt{70}$

   E. 21

9. $\dfrac{4\sqrt{15}}{6\sqrt{6}} =$

   A. $\dfrac{24\sqrt{15}}{6}$

   B. $\dfrac{3\sqrt{10}}{6}$

   C. $\dfrac{\sqrt{10}}{3}$

   D. $\sqrt{10}$

   E. 360

10. $\dfrac{15\sqrt{11}}{\sqrt{5}} =$

   A. $\dfrac{15\sqrt{11}}{5}$

   B. $\dfrac{55\sqrt{11}}{25}$

   C. $\dfrac{3\sqrt{11}}{5}$

   D. $3\sqrt{55}$

   E. $3\sqrt{11}$

11. $\dfrac{4\sqrt{3}}{\sqrt{2}} + \dfrac{2\sqrt{3}}{\sqrt{2}} =$

   A. $\dfrac{6\sqrt{3}}{2}$

   B. $\dfrac{6\sqrt{3}}{4}$

   C. $3\sqrt{6}$

   D. $6\sqrt{3}$

   E. $12\sqrt{3}$

12. $\dfrac{7}{\sqrt{5}} + \dfrac{3}{\sqrt{2}} =$

   A. $\dfrac{14\sqrt{5} + 15\sqrt{2}}{10}$

   B. $\dfrac{29\sqrt{10}}{2}$

   C. $\sqrt{10}$

   D. $\dfrac{7\sqrt{5} + 3\sqrt{2}}{5}$

   E. $\dfrac{10\sqrt{7}}{7}$

13. $\dfrac{8\sqrt{6}}{\sqrt{3}} - \dfrac{5\sqrt{3}}{\sqrt{2}} =$

   A. $\dfrac{8\sqrt{6} - 5\sqrt{3}}{5}$

   B. $\dfrac{33\sqrt{12}}{6}$

   C. $-7\sqrt{12}$

   D. $\dfrac{16\sqrt{2} - 5\sqrt{6}}{2}$

   E. $8\sqrt{2} - 15\sqrt{6}$

14. $\dfrac{6\sqrt{11}}{\sqrt{3}} - \dfrac{2\sqrt{5}}{\sqrt{2}} =$

   A. $\dfrac{6\sqrt{33} - 2\sqrt{10}}{5}$

   B. $\dfrac{2\sqrt{23}}{6}$

   C. $2\sqrt{23}$

   D. $6\sqrt{33} - 2\sqrt{10}$

   E. $2\sqrt{33} - \sqrt{10}$

15. $\dfrac{2\sqrt{2}}{\sqrt{8}} + \dfrac{7\sqrt{3}}{\sqrt{3}} =$

   A. $\dfrac{2\sqrt{2} + 7\sqrt{3}}{24}$

   B. $\dfrac{9\sqrt{5}}{11}$

   C. $\dfrac{29}{11}$

   D. $2\sqrt{2} + 7\sqrt{3}$

   E. 8

I.   Fill in the blank with the best answer. (2 points each)

1. _____   A regular polygon with five sides and five angles.

2. _____   The side opposite the right angle in a right triangle.

3. _____   A pie-shaped section of a circle.

4. _____   A solid with lateral surfaces that are parallelograms and two parallel bases.

5. _____   Any quadrilateral with four sides congruent.

6. _____   A line segment drawn between two points on a circle.

7. _____   The name of a three-dimensional circle.

8. _____   Horizontal lines that measure the north-south distance from the equator.

II.   Find the volume of a shoe box that is 10 inches by 6 inches by 4 inches. (5 points)

III.   Find the surface area of a cylinder with a diameter of 10 inches and a height of 6 inches. (5 points)

IV.   Simplify the radical expressions as completely as possible. (4 points each)

1. $(2\sqrt{6})(5\sqrt{10})$

2. $3\sqrt{7} - 2\sqrt{71} + 5\sqrt{3}$

3. $3\sqrt{7} - 2\sqrt{7} + \frac{1}{2}\sqrt{7} - \frac{3}{2}\sqrt{7}$

4. $\dfrac{\sqrt{3}}{\sqrt{6}}$

V. Assume the given polygon is regular. (4 points each)

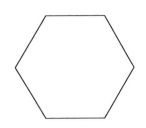

1. What is the measure of each interior angle?

2. What is the total measure of the exterior angles?

VI. Find the area and the circumference of a circle with a radius of 7 feet, using the fractional equivalent for π. (10 points)

VII. Draw an arc with a radius of 2 inches and a measure of 220°. (5 points)

VIII. Find the surface area of a pyramid with a square base and a slant height of 5 inches. One edge of the square is 4 inches. (5 points)

IX. Use the diagram below to answer the questions. (3 points each)

1. What is the measure of minor arc AXC?

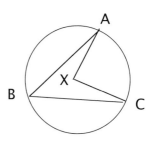

2. What is the measure of ∠ABC?

Given: X is the center of the circle.
m∠AXC = 82°

X. State the Pythagorean theorem. (4 points) Use it to find the missing sides in the figures below. (5 points each)

1.

L'   10'

6'

2.

2   √13

L

3.

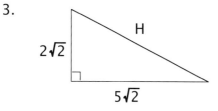

2√2   H

5√2

4.

H $\dfrac{1}{\sqrt{2}}$

$\dfrac{1}{\sqrt{3}}$

Circle your answer.

1. The side opposite the largest angle of a right triangle is the:
   A. long leg
   B. hypotenuse
   C. apothem
   D. height
   E. square

2. In a 45° – 45° – 90° triangle, the sides opposite the 45° angles are:
   A. parallel
   B. radicals
   C. similar
   D. congruent
   E. unequal

3. A 45° – 45° – 90° triangle is what kind of triangle?
   A. equilateral
   B. scalene
   C. isosceles
   D. obtuse
   E. equilangular

4. What rule is used to find the missing side of any right triangle?
   A. vertical angles
   B. definition of a triangle
   C. corresponding angles
   D. sum of interior angles
   E. the Pythagorean theorem

5. What factor is multiplied times the length of the leg to find the hypotenuse of a 45° – 45° – 90° triangle?
   A. $\sqrt{5}$
   B. $\sqrt{2}$
   C. $\sqrt{3}$
   D. 3
   E. 2

6. A right triangle has two legs, each with a length of 25. What is the length of the hypotenuse?
   A. $25\sqrt{2}$
   B. $5\sqrt{2}$
   C. 50
   D. $10\sqrt{5}$
   E. 30

7. One leg of a 45° – 45° – 90° triangle is $3\sqrt{2}$. What is the length of the hypotenuse?
   A. $3\sqrt{2}$
   B. $6\sqrt{4}$
   C. 6
   D. $6\sqrt{2}$
   E. 12

8. The hypotenuse of a 45° – 45° – 90° triangle is $9\sqrt{2}$. What is the length of one leg?
   A. 9
   B. $3\sqrt{2}$
   C. $6\sqrt{2}$
   D. 18
   E. 6

9. The hypotenuse of a 45°–45°–90° triangle is 2. What is the sum of the lengths of the legs?
   A. $\sqrt{2}$
   B. $2\sqrt{2}$
   C. 2
   D. 4
   E. $2+\sqrt{2}$

10. The sides of a triangle measure 5, 5, and $5\sqrt{2}$. What is known about the triangle?
   A. It is a right triangle.
   B. At least one angle is 45°.
   C. It is an isosceles triangle.
   D. none of the above
   E. A, B, and C

Use for #11–12.

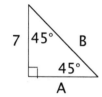

11. A =
   A. 7
   B. $\sqrt{7}$
   C. $7\sqrt{2}$
   D. $\sqrt{2}$
   E. 49

12. B =
   A. 7
   B. $\sqrt{7}$
   C. $7\sqrt{2}$
   D. $\sqrt{2}$
   E. 14

Use for #13–15.

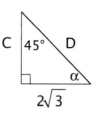

13. m∠α =
   A. 90°
   B. 60°
   C. 30°
   D. 45°
   E. none of the above

14. C =
   A. $2\sqrt{3}$
   B. $2\sqrt{2}$
   C. $2\sqrt{5}$
   D. 6
   E. none of the above

15. D =
   A. $2\sqrt{3}$
   B. $2\sqrt{2}$
   C. 12
   D. 6
   E. none of the above

Circle your answer.

1. If a triangle has a 60° and a 30° angle, the third angle will be:
    A. 30°
    B. 60°
    C. 45°
    D. 90°
    E. cannot be determined

2. A triangle with sides of three different lengths is what kind of triangle?
    A. scalene
    B. isosceles
    C. equilateral
    D. always acute
    E. always a right triangle

3. What is the relationship between the hypotenuse and the short leg of a 30° – 60° – 90° triangle? The hypotenuse is:
    A. half as long
    B. three times as long
    C. $\sqrt{3}$ times as long
    D. two times as long
    E. none of the above

4. If the hypotenuse of a 30° – 60° – 90° triangle is known, the short leg is found by:
    A. multiplying by 2
    B. dividing by 2
    C. multiplying by $\sqrt{2}$
    D. multiplying by $\sqrt{3}$
    E. dividing by $\sqrt{3}$

5. What factor is multiplied times the length of the short leg to find the long leg of a 30° – 60° – 90° triangle?
    A. $\sqrt{5}$
    B. $\sqrt{2}$
    C. $\sqrt{3}$
    D. 3
    E. 2

6. In a 30° – 60° – 90° triangle, the side opposite the 30° angle is $4\sqrt{5}$. What is the length of the hypotenuse?
    A. $8\sqrt{10}$
    B. $8\sqrt{5}$
    C. $4\sqrt{10}$
    D. $2\sqrt{5}$
    E. $16\sqrt{5}$

7. In a 30° – 60° – 90° triangle, the short side is 2A. What is the length of the hypotenuse?
    A. $4A^4$
    B. 2A
    C. $2A^2\sqrt{2}$
    D. $2A^2\sqrt{3}$
    E. 4A

8. In a 30° – 60° – 90° triangle, the hypotenuse is 14R. What is the length of the short side?
    A. $7\sqrt{R}$
    B. $14\sqrt{R}$
    C. 28R
    D. 7
    E. 7R

9. If the long leg of a 30°- 60°- 90° triangle is 12, what is the length of the short side?
  - A. $12\sqrt{3}$
  - B. $4\sqrt{3}$
  - C. $6\sqrt{2}$
  - D. 6
  - E. $2\sqrt{3}$

Use for #10–12.

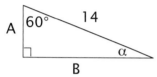

10. $m\angle\alpha$ =
  - A. 90°
  - B. 60°
  - C. 30°
  - D. 45°
  - E. none of the above

11. A =
  - A. 7
  - B. $\sqrt{7}$
  - C. $7\sqrt{2}$
  - D. $7\sqrt{3}$
  - E. 28

12. B =
  - A. 7
  - B. $\sqrt{7}$
  - C. $7\sqrt{2}$
  - D. $7\sqrt{3}$
  - E. 28

Use for #13–15.

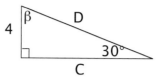

13. $m\angle\beta$ =
  - A. 90°
  - B. 60°
  - C. 30°
  - D. 45°
  - E. none of the above

14. C =
  - A. $4\sqrt{3}$
  - B. $4\sqrt{2}$
  - C. $8\sqrt{3}$
  - D. 8
  - E. none of the above

15. D =
  - A. $4\sqrt{3}$
  - B. $4\sqrt{2}$
  - C. 8
  - D. $8\sqrt{2}$
  - E. none of the above

Circle your answer.

1. Postulates are:
   I. proven
   II. unproven
   III. obvious
   IV. untrue

   A. I, III
   B. II, III
   C. II, IV
   D. IV only
   E. III only

2. Theorems are proved by use of:
   A. proven statements
   B. measurements
   C. equations
   D. correspondence
   E. postulates

3. Vertical angles are:
   A. obtuse
   B. acute
   C. congruent
   D. unequal
   E. complementary

4. The measures of the exterior angles of a polygon total:
   A. 360°
   B. 180°
   C. 90°
   D. 290°
   E. varies

5. If a parallelogram has four congruent sides, it is a(n):
   A. trapezoid
   B. rhombus
   C. rectangle
   D. concave polygon
   E. ellipse

6. If the measures of two angles add up to 90°, they are:
   A. supplementary
   B. congruent
   C. vertical
   D. complementary
   E. corresponding

7. The sum of the measures of the interior angles of a triangle is:
   A. 360°
   B. 180°
   C. 90°
   D. 290°
   E. varies

8. Two angles that have equal measures are:
   A. acute
   B. corresponding
   C. supplementary
   D. complementary
   E. congruent

9. Two angles whose measures add up to 180° are:
   A. acute
   B. corresponding
   C. supplementary
   D. complementary
   E. congruent

10. A quadrilateral with only one pair of parallel sides is a:
    A. rhombus
    B. trapezoid
    C. parallelogram
    D. rectangle
    E. square

11. If a triangle has sides R, S, and T, and $R \leq S \leq T$, then:
    A. $R + S < T$
    B. $R + S \geq T$
    C. $R + S > T$
    D. $R + S = T$
    E. $R + S \leq T$

12. A quadrilateral with two pairs of parallel sides is always a:
    A. rhombus
    B. trapezoid
    C. parallelogram
    D. rectangle
    E. square

13. If leg squared plus leg squared equals hypotenuse squared, the triangle is:
    A. equilateral
    B. right
    C. congruent
    D. scalene
    E. complementary

14. Two lines that intersect and form a right angle are:
    A. complementary
    B. bisectors
    C. collinear
    D. parallel
    E. perpendicular

15. In order for alternate interior angles to be congruent, the lines cut by the transversal must be:
    A. complementary
    B. bisectors
    C. collinear
    D. parallel
    E. perpendicular

Circle your answer.

1. If corresponding angles and sides of two triangles are congruent, the triangles are:
    A. similar
    B. congruent
    C. equilateral
    D. supplementary
    E. acute

2. What is the sum of the measures of two supplementary angles?
    A. 90°
    B. 360°
    C. 60°
    D. 180°
    E. none of the above

Use this diagram for #3–8.

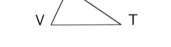

$\triangle SRQ \leftrightarrow \triangle SVT$

3. $\overline{SR}$ corresponds to:
    A. $\overline{QR}$
    B. $\overline{SV}$
    C. $\overline{RQ}$
    D. $\overline{ST}$
    E. $\overline{RV}$

4. ∠QRS corresponds to:
    A. ∠RQS
    B. ∠TSV
    C. ∠STV
    D. ∠TVS
    E. ∠VTS

5. ∠RSQ corresponds to:
    A. ∠VST
    B. ∠RQS
    C. ∠TVS
    D. ∠QRS
    E. ∠STV

6. △SRQ corresponds to:
    A. △SVT
    B. △SRQ
    C. △TSV
    D. △TVS
    E. △STV

7. $\overline{QR}$ corresponds to:
    A. $\overline{RV}$
    B. $\overline{SV}$
    C. $\overline{QS}$
    D. $\overline{ST}$
    E. $\overline{TV}$

8. ∠SVT corresponds to:
    A. ∠VST
    B. ∠SRQ
    C. ∠TVS
    D. ∠TSV
    E. ∠QSR

Use this diagram for #9–12.

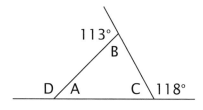

Use this diagram for #13–15.

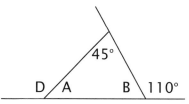

9. What is the measure of ∠C?
    A. 28°
    B. 242°
    C. 60°
    D. 62°
    E. 45°

10. What is the measure of ∠B?
    A. 118°
    B. 247°
    C. 23°
    D. 62°
    E. 67°

11. What is the measure of ∠A?
    A. 28°
    B. 51°
    C. 62°
    D. 231°
    E. 67°

12. What is the measure
    of exterior angle D?
    A. 118°
    B. 129°
    C. 113°
    D. 309°
    E. 39°

13. What is the measure of ∠B?
    A. 45°
    B. 70°
    C. 65°
    D. 250°
    E. 20°

14. What is the measure of ∠A?
    A. 45°
    B. 70°
    C. 65°
    D. 250°
    E. 20°

15. What is the measure
    of exterior angle D?
    A. 110°
    B. 45°
    C. 70°
    D. 115°
    E. 65°

24

Circle your answer.

1. We can determine the measure of an angle of a triangle if we know:
   A. one other angle
   B. two other angles
   C. one side and one angle
   D. the length of all three sides
   E. the length of two sides

2. If two triangles each have sides of 2, 6, and 7, which of the following is true?
   A. They are congruent.
   B. They have different angles.
   C. They are not congruent.
   D. They are right triangles.
   E. none of the above

3. Two right triangles each have legs of 4 and 5. Which of the following statements about the two triangles are true?

   I. They are congruent.
   II. The hypotenuse of each has the same measure.
   III. The angles of one are not congruent to the angles of the other.
   IV. The angles of one are congruent to corresponding angles of the other.

   A. I
   B. II
   C. III
   D. II, III
   E. I, II, IV

4. The reflexive property states that:
   A. A = A
   B. AB = BA
   C. A + B = B + A
   D. if A = B and B = C, then A = C
   E. $A^2 + B^2 = C^2$

5. If H is the midpoint of $\overline{GE}$, then:
   A. GH ≠ EH
   B. $\overline{GE} \cong \overline{HE}$
   C. $\overline{GH} \cong \overline{HE}$
   D. $\overline{GE} \cong \overline{GH}$
   E. GE ≠ EG

6. Vertical angles are always:
   A. supplementary
   B. right angles
   C. complementary
   D. congruent
   E. acute

7. Two triangles with three sets of sides congruent to each other may be proved congruent by:
   A. measuring angles
   B. SAS
   C. SSS
   D. the Pythagorean theorem
   E. transitive property

8. Two right triangles with congruent legs may be proved congruent by:
   A. measuring angles
   B. SAS
   C. SSS
   D. the Pythagorean theorem
   E. reflexive property

Use this diagram for #9–11.

Q, R, S, T **Given:** QRTS is a rhombus.

9. Which postulate may be used to prove $\overline{QR} \cong \overline{ST}$?
   A. definition of a rhombus
   B. SAS
   C. SSS
   D. reflexive property
   E. vertical angles

10. What postulate may be used to prove $\overline{SR} \cong \overline{SR}$?
   A. definition of a rhombus
   B. SAS
   C. SSS
   D. reflexive property
   E. transitive property

11. If $\overline{QR} \cong \overline{ST}$, $\overline{QS} \cong \overline{RT}$, $\overline{SR} \cong \overline{SR}$, what postulate may be used to prove $\triangle QRS \cong \triangle TSR$?
   A. definition of a rhombus
   B. SAS
   C. SSS
   D. reflexive property
   E. transitive property

Use this diagram for #12–14.

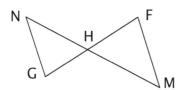

N, F, H, G, M **Given:** H is the midpoint of $\overline{NM}$ and $\overline{GF}$.

12. What postulate may be used to prove $\overline{NH} \cong \overline{HM}$?
   A. definition of a triangle
   B. SAS
   C. vertical angles
   D. definition of midpoint
   E. reflexive property

13. What may be used to prove $\angle NHG \cong \angle MHF$?
   A. definition of a triangle
   B. SAS
   C. vertical angles
   D. definition of a midpoint
   E. reflexive property

14. Given $\overline{NH} \cong \overline{HM}$, $\overline{GH} \cong \overline{HF}$, $\angle NHG \cong \angle MHF$, what may be used to prove $\triangle NHG \cong \triangle MHF$?
   A. definition of a triangle
   B. SAS
   C. SSS
   D. reflexive property
   E. Pythagorean theorem

15. Which of the following is true?
   A. Postulates must be proved before they are used to prove theorems.
   B. Postulates are unproven statements used to prove theorems.
   C. Theorems are unproven statements used to prove postulates.
   D. The words "postulate" and "theorem" may be used interchangeably.
   E. Geometric proofs must contain only statements that can be proven true by other geometric proofs.

Circle your answer.

1. Which of the following cannot be used to prove two triangles congruent?
   A. ASA
   B. SAS
   C. SSS
   D. AAS
   E. AAA

2. If two triangles are congruent, what is true of their corresponding parts?
   A. They are supplementary.
   B. They are complementary.
   C. They are rotated.
   D. They are congruent.
   E. They have no provable relationship.

3. In order to prove the shortest sides of two triangles congruent, you should first:
   A. prove the triangles congruent
   B. prove that both are equilateral
   C. find the area of the triangle
   D. find the perimeter of the triangle
   E. bisect the largest angles of each

4. Given the line QRT, if the measure of $\overline{QR}$ equals the measure of $\overline{RT}$, then R is:
   A. the origin
   B. the vertex
   C. the midpoint
   D. a bisector
   E. undetermined

5. Given triangle A and triangle B, if two of their sets of corresponding angles are congruent, what is the **minimum** additional information necessary to determine if $\Delta A \cong \Delta B$?
   A. measure of the third angle of each
   B. length of one corresponding side of each
   C. length of two corres-ponding sides of each
   D. length of all three corresponding sides of each
   E. measure of the third angle and length of one set of corresponding sides

6. If line KZ bisects angle JKX, which must be true?
   A. $\angle JKZ \cong \angle XKZ$
   B. $\overline{JK} \cong \overline{KX}$
   C. $\overline{JK} \perp \overline{KX}$
   D. $\angle JKZ$ is twice as large as $\angle XKZ$
   E. none of the above

7. A four-sided figure with two pairs of parallel lines can always be named a:
   A. square
   B. rhombus
   C. parallelogram
   D. rectangle
   E. trapezoid

8. Given two triangles each with angles of 30° and 40°, and sides between the angles with a length of 5, by what postulate can the triangles be proven congruent?
    A. SSS
    B. SAS
    C. definition of an isosceles triangle
    D. reflexive property
    E. ASA

9. Corresponding parts of congruent triangles are:
    A. similar
    B. congruent
    C. parallel
    D. unequal
    E. reflexive

Use this diagram for #10–12.

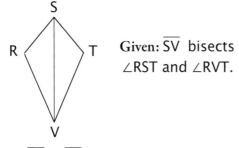

Given: $\overline{SV}$ bisects ∠RST and ∠RVT.

10. $\overline{SV} \cong \overline{SV}$ by:
    A. reflexive property
    B. transitive property
    C. SSS
    D. definition of a triangle
    E. SAS

11. ∠RSV ≅ ∠TSV by:
    A. reflexive property
    B. vertical angles
    C. SAS
    D. definition of a bisector
    E. definition of a triangle

12. If ΔSRV ≅ ΔSTV, then:
    A. $\overline{ST} \cong \overline{RV}$
    B. $\overline{RV} \cong \overline{TV}$
    C. $\overline{RS} \cong \overline{TV}$
    D. $\overline{RV} \cong \overline{SV}$
    E. none of these

Use this diagram for #13–15.

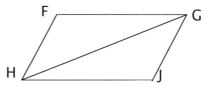

Given: FGJH is a parallelogram.

13. $\overline{FG} \parallel \overline{JH}$ by:
    A. alternate interior angles
    B. SSS
    C. definition of a bisector
    D. reflexive property
    E. definition of a parallelogram

14. ∠FGH ≅ ∠JHG by:
    A. SAS
    B. definition of a bisector
    C. alternate interior angles
    D. AAS
    E. alternate exterior angles

15. Given ∠FGH ≅ ∠JHG, ∠FHG ≅ ∠JGH, and $\overline{HG} \cong \overline{HG}$, the two triangles are congruent by:
    A. ASA
    B. AAS
    C. SAS
    D. reflexive property
    E. definition of a parallelogram

Circle your answer.

1. Right triangles can be proved congruent with less information than needed for other triangles because:
   A. all right triangles are congruent
   B. all right triangles are equilateral
   C. their angles add up to 180°
   D. all right triangles are isosceles
   E. one congruent angle is already given

2. If we know two sides of a right triangle, we can determine the third by:
   A. visual estimating
   B. Pythagorean theorem
   C. SSS postulate
   D. simple addition
   E. measuring the angles

3. If two right triangles have the hypotenuse and a leg congruent (HL), the triangles can be proved congruent by:
   A. definition of a triangle
   B. AAA
   C. the binomial theorem
   D. SSS
   E. reflexive theory

4. If two right triangles have congruent legs (LL), the triangles can be proved congruent by:
   A. SAS
   B. AAS
   C. definition of a triangle
   D. supplementary angles
   E. transitive property

5. If two right triangles have the hypotenuse and a non-right angle congruent (HA), the triangles can be proved congruent by:
   A. SAS
   B. AAS
   C. SSS
   D. supplementary angles
   E. reflexive property

6. In a right triangle, AAS is the same as:
   A. SS
   B. HA
   C. LL
   D. HL
   E. SAS

Use this diagram for #7–10.

Given: QRTS is a rectangle.

7. ∠SQR and ∠STR are right angles by:
   A. definition of a triangle
   B. the Pythagorean theorem
   C. definition of a rectangle
   D. vertical angles
   E. alternate interior angles

8. $\overline{QR}$ is congruent to $\overline{ST}$ by:
   A. definition of a triangle
   B. definition of a rectangle
   C. SSS
   D. reflexive property
   E. alternate interior angles

9. $\overline{RS}$ is congruent to $\overline{RS}$ by:
   A. definition of an equilateral triangle
   B. HL
   C. reflexive property
   D. HA
   E. LL

10. Question #7–9 prove ΔSRQ ≅ ΔRST by:
    A. HL
    B. AAA
    C. LL
    D. HA
    E. LA

Use this diagram for #11–15.

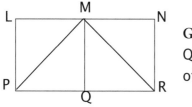

Given: $\overline{QM} \perp \overline{PR}$
Q is midpoint of $\overline{PR}$.

11. $\overline{PQ} \cong \overline{QR}$ by:
    A. reflexive property
    B. equilateral triangles
    C. definition of a rectangle
    D. congruence theorem
    E. definition of a midpoint

12. The reflexive property states that:
    A. $\overline{PQ} \cong \overline{QR}$
    B. $\overline{MQ} \cong \overline{MQ}$
    C. $\overline{MP} \cong \overline{MR}$
    D. $\overline{LP} \cong \overline{NR}$
    E. none of these

13. If $\overline{PQ} \cong \overline{QR}$ and $\overline{MQ} \cong \overline{MQ}$, then ΔPQM ≅ ΔRQM is proved congruent by which right triangle theorem?
    A. SSS
    B. HL
    C. must work out the Pythagorean theorem
    D. LL
    E. leg, non-right angle

14. Which of the following can be proved with the information given?
    A. $\overline{PM} \cong \overline{RM}$
    B. ∠MLP is a right angle
    C. ∠MNR is a right angle
    D. M is the midpoint of $\overline{LN}$
    E. $\overline{LN} \cong \overline{PR}$

15. Which of the following *cannot* be proved with the information given?
    A. $\overline{QM}$ bisects ΔPMR
    B. ∠NRQ is a right angle
    C. $\overline{PM} \cong \overline{RM}$
    D. ∠MPQ ≅ ∠MRQ
    E. m∠PMQ ≅ m∠RMQ

Circle your answer.

1. By definition, similar polygons
   A. are congruent
   B. have equal corresponding sides
   C. have the same shape but not the same size
   D. have right angles
   E. are equilateral

2. Which is **not** true of similar polygons?
   A. Corresponding sides are congruent.
   B. Corresponding angles are congruent.
   C. Corresponding sides are proportional.
   D. They have the same shape.
   E. They are not congruent.

3. What is the **minimum** information needed in order to prove two triangles similar?
   A. one set of congruent angles
   B. two sets of congruent angles
   C. three sets of congruent angles
   D. one set of congruent sides
   E. one set of congruent sides and one set of congruent angles

4. If the ratio of the hypotenuses of two similar right triangles is 1/3, which is known to be true?
   A. Both triangles are equilateral.
   B. Both triangles are isosceles.
   C. Ratio of the short legs is 1/3.
   D. Ratio of the long legs is 3/1.
   E. Length of one hypotenuse is 3.

5. Two triangles are examined. The ratio of all three sets of corresponding sides is found to be 3/5. The triangles must be:
   A. equilateral
   B. isosceles
   C. congruent
   D. similar
   E. right triangles

6. One triangle has a side of 8. A similar triangle has a corresponding side of 10. The ratio of the other corresponding sides must be:
   A. 4/5   D. 1/2
   B. 2/5   E. 1/3
   C. –4/5

7. One triangle has sides of 3, 5, and 6. Another triangle has corresponding sides of 6, 10, and 12. Which statement is true?
   A. They are right triangles.
   B. They are not similar.
   C. They are scalene with a ratio of 1/4.
   D. They are similar with a ratio of 1/2.
   E. Their corresponding angles are not equal.

8. Two right triangles each have a 45°
angle. Which **cannot** be proved?
   A. They are similar.
   B. They are isosceles.
   C. They are congruent.
   D. Their corresponding sides
      are proportional.
   E. The measure of their third
      angles is 45°.

9. If the ratio of the long legs of
similar triangles is 2/10, then the
ratio of the hypotenuses can be
written as:
   A. 4/10
   B. –1/5
   C. 5/1
   D. 10/2
   E. 1/5

Use this diagram for #10–12.

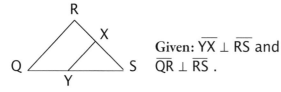

Given: $\overline{YX} \perp \overline{RS}$ and $\overline{QR} \perp \overline{RS}$.

10. ∠XSY ≅ ∠RSQ by:
    A. 180° in a triangle
    B. definition of a triangle
    C. AA postulate
    D. alternate interior angles
    E. reflexive property

11. ∠QRS and ∠YXS are right
angles because:
    A. they look like right angles.
    B. perpendicular lines form
       right angles.
    C. there are 180° in a triangle.
    D. of the Pythagorean theorem.
    E. they cannot be shown to be
       right angles.

12. If ∠QRS ≅ ∠YXS and ∠S ≅ ∠S,
then:
    A. ΔXSY and ΔRSQ are similar.
    B. ΔXSY and ΔRSQ are
       congruent.
    C. ΔXSY and ΔRSQ have no
       provable relationship.
    D. X is a midpoint
       of segment RS.
    E. Y is a midpoint
       of segment QS.

Use this diagram for #13–15.

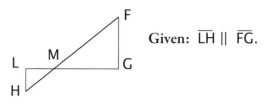

Given: $\overline{LH} \parallel \overline{FG}$.

13. ∠LMH ≅ ∠GMF by:
    A. alternate interior angles
    B. SAS
    C. AA
    D. HA
    E. vertical angles

14. ∠GFM ≅ ∠LHM by:
    A. alternate interior angles
    B. reflexive property
    C. AA
    D. definition of parallel lines
    E. vertical angles

15. ΔFGM is similar to ΔHLM by:
    A. SAS
    B. reflexive property
    C. AA
    D. AAS
    E. HA

Circle your answer.

1. Transformational geometry involves:
   A. electricity
   B. plotting equations on a grid
   C. moving and changing shapes on a grid
   D. solving equations by changing their form
   E. changing geometric proofs

2. Moving a figure over two spaces and up one space on a grid without changing the figure's shape is an example of:
   A. translation
   B. reflection
   C. rotation
   D. dilation
   E. graphing

3. A change on a grid that results in a mirror image is a:
   A. rotation
   B. translation
   C. dilation
   D. refraction
   E. reflection

4. A square drawn in the first quadrant of a grid is enlarged by a factor of 3. This is an example of:
   A. rotation
   B. dilation
   C. translation
   D. refraction
   E. reflection

5. A figure reflected in the X-axis has been:
   A. expanded
   B. contracted
   C. flipped
   D. rotated
   E. slid

6. A figure changes its location around a fixed point on a grid. This is an example of:
   A. rotation
   B. reduction
   C. dilation
   D. refraction
   E. reflection

7. When plotting a rotation, the direction of the change is always:
   A. up
   B. down
   C. right
   D. clockwise
   E. counterclockwise

8. The unit of measurement used for the movement of a rotation is:
   A. degrees
   B. squares on the grid
   C. inches
   D. centimeters
   E. unit varies

Use this diagram for #9–11.

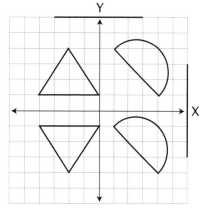

Use this diagram for #12–15.

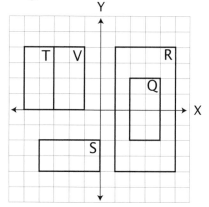

9. The triangle in the figure has undergone a:
   A. translation
   B. rotation
   C. reflection
   D. dilation
   E. refraction

10. The semicircle has undergone a:
    A. translation of one space
    B. translation of five spaces
    C. reflection on the X–axis
    D. rotation of 90°
    E. dilation of one

11. To get from the vertical line to the horizontal line, there was a:
    A. translation of five spaces down
    B. reflection on the Y–axis
    C. rotation of 90° around the origin
    D. rotation of 180° around the origin
    E. dilation

12. Which of the figures is a dilation of Q around point (3,0)?
    A. R
    B. S
    C. T
    D. V
    E. none

13. Which figure is a reflection of T on the Y–axis?
    A. Q
    B. R
    C. S
    D. V
    E. none

14. Which figure is a translation of Q left five and up two?
    A. R
    B. S
    C. T
    D. V
    E. none

15. Which figure *includes* a 90° rotation of Q?
    A. R
    B. S
    C. T
    D. V
    E. none

GEOMETRY

Circle your answer.

1. The study of trigonometry is the study of:
   A. triangles
   B. graphs
   C. rectangles
   D. area
   E. none of the above

2. Trigonometric ratios are based on what kind of triangle?
   A. equilateral
   B. acute
   C. right
   D. isosceles
   E. none of the above

3. The ratio $\frac{\text{adjacent}}{\text{hypotenuse}}$ is the:

   A. sine
   B. tangent
   C. cotangent
   D. cosine
   E. none of the above

4. The ratio $\frac{\text{opposite}}{\text{adjacent}}$ is the:

   A. tangent
   B. cotangent
   C. sine
   D. cosine
   E. none of the above

5. The ratio $\frac{\text{hypotenuse}}{\text{opposite}}$ is the:
   A. sine
   B. cosine
   C. tangent
   D. cotangent
   E. none of the above

Use this triangle for #6–8.

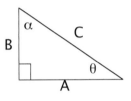

6. The value of sin θ is:
   A. $\frac{A}{C}$
   B. $\frac{B}{C}$
   C. $\frac{A}{B}$
   D. $\frac{B}{A}$
   E. $\frac{C}{B}$

7. The value of tan α is:
   A. $\frac{B}{A}$
   B. $\frac{A}{B}$
   C. $\frac{B}{C}$
   D. $\frac{C}{B}$
   E. $\frac{A}{C}$

Use this triangle for #6–8.

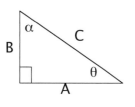

8. The value of cos θ is:
    A. $\frac{B}{A}$

    B. $\frac{A}{B}$

    C. $\frac{B}{C}$

    D. $\frac{C}{B}$

    E. $\frac{A}{C}$

Use this triangle for #9–12.

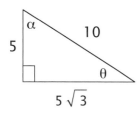

9. The value of cos θ is:

    A. $\frac{\sqrt{3}}{2}$

    B. $\frac{1}{2}$

    C. $\sqrt{3}$

    D. $\frac{\sqrt{3}}{3}$

    E. $\frac{1}{\sqrt{3}}$

10. The value of sin α is:

    A. $\frac{\sqrt{3}}{2}$

    B. $\frac{1}{2}$

    C. $\sqrt{3}$

    D. $\frac{\sqrt{3}}{3}$

    E. $\frac{1}{\sqrt{3}}$

11. The value of tan θ is

    A. 3

    B. 2

    C. $\sqrt{3}$

    D. $\frac{\sqrt{3}}{3}$

    E. $\frac{1}{2}$

12. Based on your knowledge of special triangles, the measure of ∠θ is:
    A. 45°
    B. 90°
    C. 30°
    D. 60°
    E. 80°

Use this triangle for #13–15.

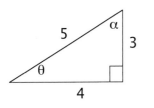

13. The value of cos θ is:

    A. $\dfrac{3}{5}$

    B. $\dfrac{3}{4}$

    C. $\dfrac{4}{5}$

    D. $\dfrac{5}{4}$

    E. $\dfrac{4}{3}$

14. The value of sin θ is:

    A. $\dfrac{3}{5}$

    B. $\dfrac{3}{4}$

    C. $\dfrac{4}{5}$

    D. $\dfrac{5}{4}$

    E. $\dfrac{4}{3}$

15. The value of tan θ is:

    A. $\dfrac{3}{5}$

    B. $\dfrac{3}{4}$

    C. $\dfrac{4}{5}$

    D. $\dfrac{5}{4}$

    E. $\dfrac{4}{3}$

Circle your answer.

1. The reciprocal of the sine is:
   A. cosine
   B. cosecant
   C. secant
   D. cotangent
   E. none of the above

2. The reciprocal of the cosine is:
   A. sine
   B. tangent
   C. cotangent
   D. secant
   E. none of the above

3. The reciprocal of the tangent is:
   A. sine
   B. cotangent
   C. cosine
   D. cosecant
   E. none of the above

4. The ratio $\frac{adjacent}{opposite}$ is the:
   A. sine
   B. tangent
   C. cosecant
   D. cosine
   E. none of the above

5. The ratio $\frac{hypotenuse}{adjacent}$ is the:
   A. secant
   B. cotangent
   C. sine
   D. cosine
   E. none of the above

6. The ratio $\frac{hypotenuse}{opposite}$ is the:
   A. tangent
   B. cosine
   C. cosecant
   D. cotangent
   E. none of the above

Use this triangle for #7–9.

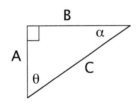

7. The value of sec θ is:

   A. $\frac{B}{C}$

   B. $\frac{A}{C}$

   C. $\frac{B}{A}$

   D. $\frac{C}{A}$

   E. $\frac{A}{B}$

8. The value of cos θ is:

   A. $\frac{B}{C}$

   B. $\frac{A}{C}$

   C. $\frac{A}{B}$

   D. $\frac{C}{B}$

   E. $\frac{C}{A}$

9. The value of csc α is:

    A. $\dfrac{C}{A}$

    B. $\dfrac{B}{C}$

    C. $\dfrac{A}{C}$

    D. $\dfrac{C}{B}$

    E. $\dfrac{A}{B}$

Use this triangle
for #10–12.

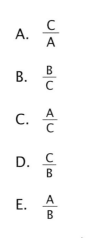

10. The value of cot 30° is:

    A. $\dfrac{\sqrt{3}}{3}$

    B. $\dfrac{1}{2}$

    C. $\sqrt{3}$

    D. $\dfrac{2\sqrt{3}}{3}$

    E. 2

11. The value of sec 60° is:

    A. $\dfrac{\sqrt{3}}{2}$

    B. $\dfrac{1}{2}$

    C. $\sqrt{3}$

    D. $\dfrac{2\sqrt{3}}{3}$

    E. 2

12. The value of csc 30° is:

    A. 3

    B. 2

    C. $\sqrt{3}$

    D. $\dfrac{\sqrt{3}}{3}$

    E. $\dfrac{1}{2}$

Use this triangle
for #13–15.

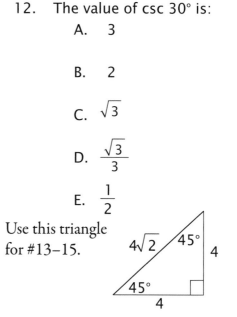

13. A version of the Pythagorean
    theorem derived from
    trigonometric ratios is:

    A. sin θ + cos θ = 1
    B. sin θ + tan θ = 1
    C. sec θ + cos θ = 1
    D. $\sin^2\theta + \cos^2\theta = 1$
    E. $\sin^2\theta + \cot^2\theta = 1$

14. The value of csc 45° is:

    A. $\dfrac{\sqrt{2}}{2}$

    B. $\dfrac{\sqrt{2}}{4}$

    C. 1

    D. $4\sqrt{2}$

    E. $\sqrt{2}$

15. The value of cot 45° is:

    A. $\dfrac{\sqrt{2}}{2}$

    B. $\dfrac{\sqrt{2}}{4}$

    C. 1

    D. $4\sqrt{2}$

    E. $\sqrt{2}$

I. Fill in the blank with the best answer. (2 points each)

1. _____   Assumed to be true; cannot be proven; an observation.

2. _____   A figure which has been enlarged or reduced without changing its shape.

3. _____   A figure which has been flipped in a line to form a mirror image.

4. _____   A function defined as the opposite over the adjacent side.

5. _____   A function defined as the hypotenuse over the adjacent side.

6. _____   Two geometric figures whose corresponding angles are congruent and whose corresponding sides have the same ratio.

7. _____   The name of a three-dimensional circle.

8. _____   The trigonometric function that is the reciprocal of the tangent.

II.   Translate the figure over one and down two. (4 points)

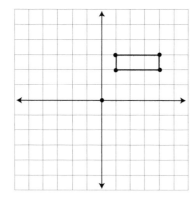

III. Find the measures of the unmarked sides of these right triangles.
     (5 points each)

1.

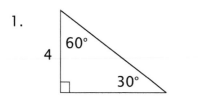

2.

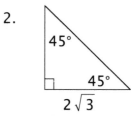

3.

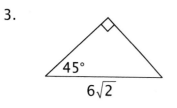

4.

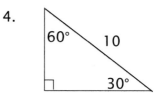

IV. Find the values of the following trigonometric functions for the triangle.
(3 points each)

1. sin θ

2. cos θ

3. tan θ

4. csc θ

5. sec θ

6. cot θ

V. If the perimeter of triangle ABC is 12, what is the value of X?
Is this a right triangle? (6 points)

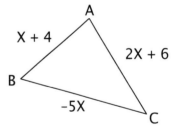

VI. Write a proof for each of the following. (12 points each)

1.

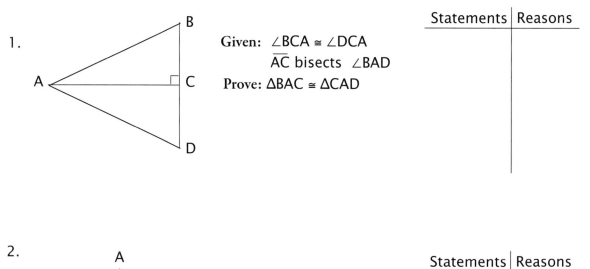

Given: ∠BCA ≅ ∠DCA
$\overline{AC}$ bisects ∠BAD
Prove: ΔBAC ≅ ΔCAD

Statements	Reasons

2.

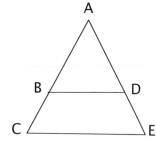

Given: $\overline{BD} \parallel \overline{CE}$
Prove: ΔACE ~ ΔABD

Statements	Reasons

3.

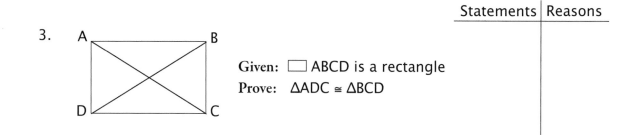

Given: ▭ ABCD is a rectangle
Prove: ΔADC ≅ ΔBCD

Statements	Reasons

I.   Fill in the blank with the best answer. (3 points each)

1. _____   The trigonometric function defined as "the adjacent side over the hypotenuse."

2. _____   An angle with a measure greater than 90° but less than 180°.

3. _____   A piece of the circumference of a circle.

4. _____   Any two angles whose measures add to 90°.

5. _____   An infinite number of connected lines lying in the same flat surface; it has length and width; two dimensional.

6. _____   A four-sided polygon with two parallel sides and two sides that are not parallel.

7. _____   A rectangular solid with all edges having the same length.

8. _____   Two or more points in the same line.

9. _____   Having the same size and shape.

10. _____   Distance around any two-dimensional geometric shape.

II. Given the drawing at right, answer the following questions. (3 points each)

1. What kind of quadrilateral is quadrilateral ABDE?

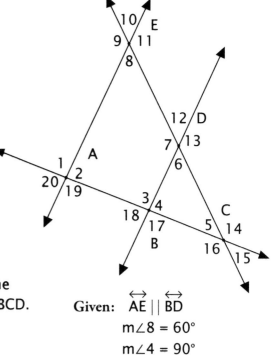

2. What angle(s) correspond(s) to ∠10?
   (give all answers)

3. m∠6 = _____ °

4. m∠5 = _____ °

5. Given that segment DC is 8 inches, find the
   lengths of the other two sides of triangle BCD.

   Given: $\overleftrightarrow{AE} \parallel \overleftrightarrow{BD}$
   m∠8 = 60°
   m∠4 = 90°

6. m∠14 = _____ °

7. Is m∠2 = m∠11?   Why or why not?

8. Name all the labeled points that are not collinear with point B in the drawing.

9. ΔBCD ~ ΔACE
   Using your answers from #5 above, find the length of the segment AE
   if CE = 20.

10. Using your answers from #5 and #9, what is the length of segment AB?

III. Write a proof for each of the following. (12 points each)

1.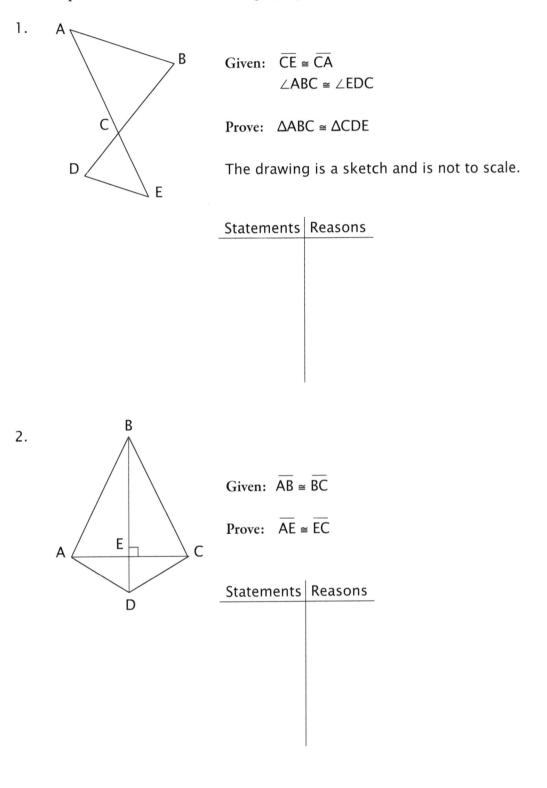

Given: $\overline{CE} \cong \overline{CA}$

$\angle ABC \cong \angle EDC$

Prove: $\triangle ABC \cong \triangle CDE$

The drawing is a sketch and is not to scale.

Statements	Reasons

2.

Given: $\overline{AB} \cong \overline{BC}$

Prove: $\overline{AE} \cong \overline{EC}$

Statements	Reasons

IV.   Graph the reflection of the triangle about the Y–axis. (5 points)

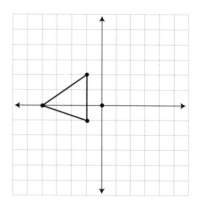

V.   Find the volume of a sphere if the radius is given as 3 cm. (5 points)

VI.   Find the surface area of a rectangular solid with edges of lengths 2 cm, 5 cm, and 7 cm. (5 points)

VII.   The measure of an exterior angle of a regular polygon is 45°.
Name the shape of the polygon. (5 points)

VIII.   Simplify the following radical expressions, if possible. Reduce to the simplest terms. (4 points each)

1. $(3\sqrt{2})(4\sqrt{22})$

2. $\dfrac{4}{\sqrt{3}} - \dfrac{2\sqrt{6}}{\sqrt{2}}$

3. $-3\sqrt{5} + \sqrt{5}$

4. $\sqrt{2} + \sqrt{3} + \sqrt{4} + \sqrt{1}$

IX.   Given that the circumference of a circle is 8π, find the radius. (5 points)

X.   Draw a segment four inches long. Now construct the perpendicular bisector to that segment. Measure your results to check. (5 points)

XI.   If the length of the minor arc AC in the diagram below is $98°$, give the the measures of the central angle and the inscribed angle shown. (5 points)

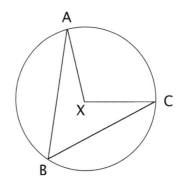

Given: X is the center of the circle.

XII. If the hypotenuse of a right triangle is 5 cm and one leg is 2 cm, what is the measurement of the other leg? (5 points)

XIII. Given that $\sin \theta = \dfrac{3}{5}$, find the values of the other 5 trigonometry functions. (10 points)